WHAT'S THE BEST TRIVIA BOOK

LOUIS RICHARDS

ISBN: 978-3-910282-01-8

OUR **HAND-PICKED**
BOOK SELECTION **FOR YOU.**

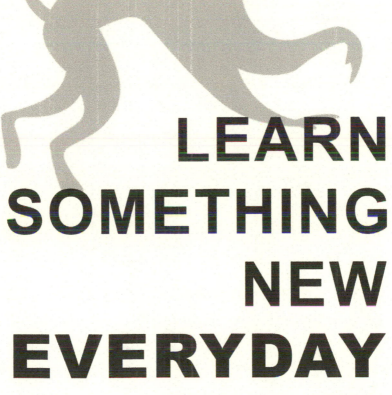

LEARN SOMETHING NEW EVERYDAY

MONKEY
PUBLISHING

CONTENT

LOUIS RICHARDS

WHAT'S THE
BEST TRIVIA
BOOK?

ANIMAL
TRIVIA

LOUIS RICHARDS

DID YOU KNOW?

LOUIS RICHARDS

HORSES SLEEP ONLY 2 HOURS A DAY ON AVERAGE.

ANIMALS

HOW DO YOU FEEL?

START

1. What cartoon family had a pet named Dino?

2. What color are the spots on a common lady bug?

3. What mammals use echolocation to fly?

4. Which sea creature has the largest brain?

5. What was the name of the first dog in outer space?

6. According to Innuit people, what is a Nanook?

7. What is the name for the offspring of a female horse and a male donkey?

8. What animal is used in the symbol for modern medicine?

9. Who rode the famous horse Nelson?

10. What kind of animal is a mandrill?

11. What is the name for a group of frogs?

12. Which common farm animal is known to be colorblind?

13. What reptile has the longest lifespan?

14. Through which part of their bodies do dogs sweat?

15. In the movie Free Willy, what kind of mammal was Willy?

16. What animal consistently gives birth to same-sex twins?

17. What insect is known for eating its mate after reproduction?

18. What's a bald eagle's nest called?

19. What's the most venomous snake in North America?

FINISH

20. Lincoln Park Zoo bought its first animal in 1874 for $10; what was it?

Answers 1. The Flintstones | 2. Black | 3. Bats | 4. Sperm whale | 5. Laika | 6. A Polar bear 7. A mule | 8. Snake | 9. George Washington | 10. Monkey | 11. Army | 12. Cow | 13. The Giant Tortoise | 14. Paw pads | 15. An Orca or "killer whale" | 16. Armadillo | 17. Praying mantis 18. Aerie (variant of eyrie) | 19. The eastern diamondback rattlesnake | 20. A bear cub

LOUIS RICHARDS

START

21 What land animal is the second heaviest?

22 What ape species is the largest?

23 What is the name of Dorothy's dog in the movie The Wizard of Oz?

24 What is the common name of a Mus musculus?

25 What percentage of all mammal species are bats?

26 How long is an elephant pregnant before it gives birth?

27 What animal (besides humans) is the only animal that can catch leprosy?

28 Which animal is known to spend 90% of its day sleeping?

29 What is the name of an animal that can live on land or in the water?

30 What is the loudest insect in the world?

31 What is the name for a female donkey?

32 What is the term for a fruit-eating animal?

33 What animal can sleep for 3 years and only mates once in its life?

34 What animal symbolized the Egyptian god Sobek?

35 What is the name for a group of bats?

36 Which ant has the most painful sting?

37 What kind of animal produces the substance gossamer?

38 What is the largest mammal in the world?

39 What is the largest deer species?

FINISH

40 What animal is used in the Toys-R-Us logo?

Answers 21. Rhinoceros (White rhino) | 22. Gorilla | 23. Toto | 24. Mouse | 25. About 20% | 26. 22 months | 27. The armadillo | 28. Koalas | 29. Amphibians | 30. Cicada | 31. Jenny or Jennet | 32. Frugivore | 33. Snail | 34. Crocodile | 35. Murder | 36. Bullet ant | 37. Spider | 38. Blue Whale | 39. Moose | 40. Giraffe

ANIMALS

41 What type of bird is the Macaw?

42 What intestinal parasite affects both man and animals?

43 Which two famous bears lived at Jellystone Park?

44 What is the smartest farm animal?

45 What animal is the national mammal of the United States?

46 What animal symbolizes the World Wide Fund for Nature?

47 Chi Chi and An An were what kind of animals?

48 What is a mole's main food source?

49 Which American president kept raccoons in the White House?

50 What is it called when a caterpillar turns into a butterfly?

51 What is the only male animal known to give birth?

52 What was the name of Tarzan's chimpanzee friend?

53 An ocelot is what color?

54 What color are giraffes' tongues?

55 What animal produces young that are named foals?

56 What is the sacred animal of Thailand?

57 What kind of animal only eats plants?

58 How many bones do sharks have?

59 What animal became the world's first mammal to be successfully cloned?

60 How many hearts does an earthworm have?

61 What is the common name for a Lupus?

62 What is the formal name for the study of animals?

63 What is the name for a group of lions?

64 What animal never sleeps?

65 Which body part helps an insect to navigate tight spaces?

66 What bird takes over the nests of other species?

67 How many legs does a spider have?

68 Lemurs are native to which country?

69 What is the name for a queen bee's closest servants?

70 In Peru, it is common to eat which popular household pet?

71 How many hearts does an octopus have?

72 What sea creature has the largest eyes?

73 Which mammal is not able to jump?

74 What animals live in an apiary enclosure?

75 What is the name for a fox's home?

76 If reptiles are in the class Reptila, birds are in which class?

77 What animal (besides humans) is the only animal to have unique prints?

78 What are rhino horns made of?

79 What reptile cannot stick out its tongue?

80 Where is the largest natural population of Asian elephants?

Answers | 61. Wolf | 62. Zoology | 63. Pride | 64. Bullfrog | 65. Antennae | 66. Cuckoo | 67. Eight | 68. Madagascar | 69. Drones | 70. The guinea pig | 71. Three | 72. The colossal squid | 73. Elephant | 74. Bees | 75. A den | 76. Aves | 77. Koala bears | 78. Keratin | 79. Crocodile | 80. India

ANIMALS

81 Tasmanian Devils, Koalas, and Kangaroos are members of which group of mammals?

82 What is the only animal born with horns?

83 What kind of animal is a Komodo dragon?

84 What is the slowest animal in the world?

85 Which species of fish is Nemo?

86 What is the formal name for the study of bird eggs?

87 What species of penguin is the largest?

88 What is the name for animals that do not eat meat?

89 What insect is known for having the best eyesight?

90 How many stomachs does a cow have?

91 How many stages does a complete metamorphosis have?

92 The male elephant is known as a bull. What is the name of the female elephant?

93 Which bird is unable to move their eyes?

94 What is the name of Walt Disney's famous animated deer?

95 Which bird is known to have eyes larger than its brain?

96 Which animal has the thickest fur of any mammal?

97 How do otters avoid drifting apart while they sleep?

98 What color is the blood of an octopus?

99 How many of the 250+ known species of shark are dangerous to humans?

100 What is the term for animals without backbones?

Answers 81. They're all marsupials | **82.** Giraffes | **83.** Lizard | **84.** Sloth (Three-toed sloth) | **85.** Clownfish | **86.** Oology | **87.** Emperor | **88.** Herbivore | **89.** Dragonfly | **90.** Four | **91.** Four, egg, larva, pupa and adult | **92.** Cow | **93.** Owl | **94.** Bambi | **95.** Ostrich | **96.** Sea otter | **97.** Hold each others paws | **98.** Blue | **99.** Eight | **100.** Invertebrates

LOUIS RICHARDS

WHAT'S THE
BEST TRIVIA
BOOK?

NATURE & SCIENCE
TRIVIA

DID YOU KNOW?

LOUIS RICHARDS

HUMAN DNA
AND BANANA DNA ARE 50% THE SAME.

NATURE & SCIENCE

HOW DO YOU FEEL?

1. What does the constellation name Corona Borealis mean?

2. How many bones does the average human being have?

3. What Russian physiologist studied the reflexive behavior of dogs?

4. What causes a solar eclipse?

5. What is the formal name for the study of air movement and objects moving through the air?

6. Which bear's footprint is distinct due to its 5 claw marks?

7. What vitamin deficiency causes scurvy?

8. What bird is the only one that can fly backward?

9. What temperature is considered to be absolute zero?

10. What is the largest bone in the human body?

11. What is the chemical symbol for lead?

12. What field would you work in if you studied histology?

13. What are the ingredients of gunpowder, besides potassium nitrate?

14. Who was the first American woman astronaut to visit space?

15. What does NASA stand for?

16. What was the name of the first supersonic passenger-carrying commercial airplane?

17. What was the first planet discovered with a telescope?

18. Cocci, spirilla, and streptococci are examples of?

19. What is the smallest unit of matter?

20. What is the largest organ in the human body?

Answers 1. Northern Crown | 2. 206 | 3. Ivan Pavlov | 4. The Moon moving through the Sun and the Earth, casting a shadow on Earth. | 5. Aerodynamics | 6. Grizzly | 7. Vitamin C | 8. The hummingbird | 9. -273 Degrees C or Kelvin - 459 degrees F | 10. The femur (the thigh bone) | 11. Pb | 12. Cells | 13. Sulphur & charcoal | 14. Sally Ride became the first American woman in space in 1983. | 15. National Aeronautics and Space Administration | 16. Concorde | 17. Uranus | 18. Bacteria | 19. The atom | 20. Skin

21 What is the smallest planet in the Solar System?

22 What part of the plant conducts photosynthesis?

23 What animal (besides humans) has sex for reasons of pleasure, not only reproduction?

24 Who's law states "For every action, there is an equal and opposite reaction"?

25 Can you hear anything in outer space?

26 What is the name for a growing method that does not use soil?

27 If a female honeybee receives royal jelly as a larva, what will it become?

28 What's the most abundant element in the universe?

29 Where are the three smallest bones in the human body located?

30 Which nation is responsible for inventing the wheelbarrow?

31 How many states of matter are there?

32 What hormone does the pancreas produce?

33 Besides fingerprints, a unique print can also be found in this part of the mouth.

34 Who is considered to be the man who invented the telephone?

35 Is earth's gravitational pull stronger at the poles or the equator?

36 The sun consists mainly of these two elements.

37 Which scientist proposed the theory of relativity?

38 What is the name scientists use for how the universe will collapse?

39 The Himalayan yeti is also known as what?

40 What do the letters URL stand for in relation to computers?

Answers 21. *Mercury* | 22. *Leaves (Chloroplasts)* | 23. *Dolphin* | 24. *Newton's* | 25. *No, sound has no way to travel.* | 26. *Hydroponics* | 27. *Queen* | 28. *Hydrogen* | 29. *In the middle ear (the malleus, incus and stapes)* | 30. *The Chinese, circa 200 A.D.* | 31. *Four: Solid, liquid, gas and plasma.* | 32. *Insulin* | 33. *The tongue* | 34. *Alexander Graham Bell* | 35. *Equator* | 36. *Hydrogen and helium* | 37. *Albert Einstein* | 38. *The Big Crunch* | 39. *The abominable snowman* | 40. *Uniform Resource Locator*

NATURE & SCIENCE

START

41 What are the ulna, radius and clavicle?

42 What are the 2 components of complex numbers?

43 What is the center of an atom is called?

44 How many legs are on each segment of a millipede?

45 Water is composed of which two elements?

46 Who is the father of the child who flew too close to the sun with feathers held together by wax?

47 What is the name of the system blind people use to read?

48 What do chiropodists treat?

49 How long has the earth been around?

50 What system is measured in farads?

51 Where is the carotid artery located?

52 What type of animal are frogs?

53 Who discovered Penicillin?

54 Nyctophobia is the fear of what?

55 Who was the inventor of the Centigrade scale?

56 How many teeth do adults have?

57 In chemistry, ATP stands for what?

58 The mitochondria is the _____ of the cell.

59 Which astronomer discovered that the sun was the center of the solar system?

FINISH

60 A woman's ceasing of menstruation is known as what?

Answers 41. Bones | 42. Real and imaginary | 43. Nucleus | 44. 4 legs | 45. Hydrogen and oxygen | 46. Daedalus | 47. Braille | 48. The feet | 49. The earth is about 4.5 billion years old. | 50. Capacitance | 51. In the neck | 52. Amphibians | 53. Sir Alexander Fleming | 54. The dark | 55. Anders Celsius | 56. 32 teeth. | 57. Adenosine triphosphate, the molecule that is used for energy by all cells | 58. Powerhouse | 59. Nicolaus Copernicus | 60. Menopause

61 What is Polyvinyl Chloride better known as?

62 Which part of the brain does a lobotomy effect?

63 What is the name of the comet that appears roughly once every 76 years?

64 What were pterosaurs?

65 Which female pilot was the first to fly solo across the Atlantic Ocean?

66 Where is earth's largest meteor crater?

67 What are fly larvae called?

68 What does ROM stand for in computer terminology?

69 Brass is made of what two metals?

70 Which planet spins faster than the rest?

71 What are the 3 parts of an insect's body?

72 Which star is closest to the earth (besides the sun)?

73 What substance do hair and fingernails consist of?

74 Who is given the credit for discovering electricity?

75 A Geiger counter measures what?

76 What two-dimensional shape has four equal sides but no right angles?

77 Which country produced the first alarm clock?

78 Why was the seismosaurus given its name?

79 What kind of creature is kept by an apiarist?

80 E.J. Claghorn patented what vehicular safety device?

Answers 61. PVC | 62. The frontal lobe | 63. Halley's Comet (1P/Halley) | 64. Flying reptiles related to dinosaurs | 65. Amelia Earhart | 66. In South Africa (Vredefort crater) | 67. Maggots | 68. Read Only Memory | 69. Copper and zinc | 70. Jupiter is the fastest spinning planet in our solar system rotating on average once in just under 10 hours. | 71. Head, thorax & abdomen | 72. Proxima Centauri (aka Alpha Centauri) | 73. Keratin | 74. Benjamin Franklin | 75. Radiation | 76. A rhombus | 77. Germany in 1360 | 78. Because of its size, hence Earth-shaking lizard | 79. Bees | 80. The seatbelt

81 Which American car was patented in 1909?

82 Optics is the study of what?

83 What is the name of the instrument used to measure atmospheric pressure?

84 What was trepanning used for?

85 What is the road from Alaska to Chile called?

86 What is the name of the largest moon of Saturn?

87 What person is known as the father of medicine?

88 Which star is the brightest visible star from earth?

89 How many humps does a dromedary have?

90 What term is used to describe having two different colored eyes?

91 During hibernation, a bear will lose up to 25% of what?

92 What are the most common colors people will confuse when they are color blind?

93 What country has the longest coastline?

94 What is the second most common element on planet earth?

95 The interaction between a clownfish and an anemone is an example of a _____ relationship.

96 What is the fastest flying bird in the world?

97 What language does the term eureka come from?

98 What is the opposite of matter?

99 What is the oldest species of tree still alive on planet earth?

100 The coffee tree is native to what country?

Answers 81. Ford Model T | 82. Light | 83. Barometer | 84. An ancient form of medicine which involved making holes in human skull to relieve pressure; don't try this at home! | 85. The Pan-American Highway | 86. Titan | 87. Hippocrates | 88. Sirius | 89. One hump | 90. Heterochromia | 91. Body weight | 92. Red and green | 93. Canada, due to the number of northern islands. | 94. Silicon | 95. Symbiotic | 96. The Peregrine falcon | 97. Greek | 98. Antimatter | 99. A bristlecone pine in California... it's about 5000 years old! | 100. Ethiopia

GEOGRAPHY TRIVIA

Did You Know?

The shortest commercial flight
lasts only 2 minutes.
It takes place between
two islands in Scotland.

GEOGRAPHY

1 Where is the Gumbo Limbo trail?

2 Which river marks part of the boundary between Mexico and the United States?

3 Which island country lies immediately to the west of Mauritius?

4 What season begins in the Southern Hemisphere in September?

5 What is the name of the river that runs through Paris, France?

6 What navigation marker touches the mouth of the Amazon River and Lake Victoria?

7 Which is Europe's second largest country?

8 In which country is the Suez Canal located?

9 In which state of the U.S. can you find Mount Rushmore?

10 Which National Park has the deepest lake in the U.S.?

11 What is the biggest port in the United States?

12 In which U.S. state is Galveston Bay located?

13 What is South America's highest peak in the Andes, Argentina?

14 If you drove in a straight line from Moscow to Madrid how many countries would you drive through altogether?

15 What is the largest river system in North America?

16 Name the Great Lake known as the principal source of the Nile River.

17 The Rio Grande river rises from which mountain range?

18 Which strait separates Alaska from Russia?

19 Eight U.S. states are named after rivers. Name at least 3.

20 Who is credited for renaming the South Sea as the Pacific Ocean in the early 1500s?

Answers 1. Everglades National Park | **2.** Rio Grande | **3.** Réunion | **4.** Spring | **5.** The Seine | **6.** The Equator | **7.** The Ukraine | **8.** Egypt | **9.** South Dakota | **10.** Crater Lake National Park | **11.** Port of Los Angeles | **12.** Texas | **13.** Aconcagua | **14.** Eight (Russia, Belarus, Poland, Czech Republic, Germany, Switzerland, France & Spain) | **15.** The Mississippi River | **16.** Lake Victoria | **17.** Colorado Rocky Mountains | **18.** The Bering Strait | **19.** Mississippi, Missouri, Colorado, Delaware, Ohio, Tennessee, Illinois, Arkansas | **20.** Ferdinand Magellan

GEOGRAPHY

START

21 Name the largest mountain range in the eastern United States.

22 If a section of shallow ocean water is separated from deeper waters by a coral reef or sand bar, what term would describe it?

23 In which Italian city is Mt. Vesuvius located?

24 What island is Pearl Harbor on?

25 In which city is Notre Dame?

26 What's the name of Australia's biggest port?

27 What is Gulf of California is also known as?

28 Which mountain peak in Mexico is the second tallest?

29 Name the 5 oceans of the world.

30 What was the highest mountain in the world before the discovery of Everest?

31 What was the first U.S. National Park?

32 Name the capital of Colorado.

33 Which country has the most countries bordering it?

34 In which ocean is Greenland located?

35 What's the second largest country in the world?

36 If its 4:00pm in Seattle, Washington what time is it in Portland, Oregon?

37 What term describes the deepest part of the ocean?

38 What is the name of the largest sea on earth?

39 Tallahassee is the capital of which U.S. state?

FINISH

40 What are the names of the 3 biggest waterfalls in the world?

Answers 21. *The Appalachians* | 22. *A lagoon* | 23. *Naples* | 24. *Oahu* | 25. *Paris* | 26. *Sydney* | 27. *The Sea of Cortez* | 28. *Popocatepetl* | 29. *Pacific Ocean, Atlantic Ocean, Indian Ocean, Arctic Ocean and Antarctic Ocean.* | 30. *Kangchenjunga, presumed as the highest from 1847 until 1852* | 31. *Yellowstone* | 32. *Denver* | 33. *China (14)* | 34. *Arctic* | 35. *Canada* | 36. *4:00pm* | 37. *Abyss* | 38. *The South China Sea* | 39. *Florida* | 40. *Niagara, Angel and Iguazu Falls*

GEOGRAPHY

41 Death Valley is located in which U.S. state?

42 What museum, located in France, is the largest in the world?

43 Which U.S. city is named after the general who won Texas' independence from Mexico?

44 What is the name of the famous American military base in Cuba?

45 Which European country has a name that literally means lower lands?

46 Which U.S. state is also known as "The Land of 1,000 Lakes"?

47 What has been the capital of Egypt over the last thousand years?

48 In what mountain range is Kicking Horse Pass?

49 What's the highest mountain in the 48 contiguous U.S. states?

50 Where in the United States was the original London Bridge relocated?

51 How many U.S. states share a border with Mexico?

52 Which 4 countries are located in The Alps?

53 What does Copenhagen mean in English?

54 Can you give me the two former names of the modern Turkish capital of Istanbul?

55 Which famous Scottish Loch is the second largest?

56 Which states don't share a border with any other U.S. states?

57 What is the name of the largest desert in the world?

58 Which Islands were the subject of a war between Argentina and Britain in 1982?

59 Into what body of water does the Yukon River flow?

60 The Great Pyramid presides over which plateau on the outskirts of Cairo?

HOW ⊶○
DO YOU ⊶○
FEEL? ☺○

GEOGRAPHY

WHAT'S THE
BEST TRIVIA
BOOK?

14

61 Into where does the Volga (Europe's longest river) flow?

62 Denmark, Norway and Sweden combine to make what?

63 Which city is the farthest south: Seattle, Bordeaux, or Toronto?

64 What formation separates Spain and Morocco?

65 What's the name of Puerto Rico's capital?

66 Can you give me the capital of the following three countries: Syria, Morocco and Libya?

67 Where is the Great Canyon Park located?

68 What is the name of the largest lake in Europe?

69 What is Iran's capital city?

70 What is the northernmost U.S. state capital?

71 Name the desert located in southeast California.

72 Five U.S. states are located along the coast of the Pacific Ocean, name at least three of them.

73 Which is the least populated U.S. state?

74 Name the capital city of The Bahamas.

75 Which two countries are closest to the South Pole?

76 What tourist attraction is wearing away at a rate of 5 feet per year?

77 What is the tallest mountain in all of the United States?

78 What European country is the smallest independent state on the map?

79 Ouagadougou is the capital of which African country?

80 Which state was the last to join the United States?

Answers 61. *The Caspian Sea* | **62.** *Scandinavia* | **63.** *Toronto* | **64.** *The Straits of Gibraltar* | **65.** *San Juan* | **66.** *Damascus, Rabat, Tripoli* | **67.** *Arizona* | **68.** *Lake Ladoga* | **69.** *Teheran* | **70.** *Juneau, Alaska* | **71.** *Mojave* | **72.** *California, Oregon, Washington, Alaska or Hawaii* | **73.** *Wyoming* | **74.** *Nassau* | **75.** *Argentina and Chile* | **76.** *Niagara Falls* | **77.** *Mount McKinley* | **78.** *Vatican City* | **79.** *Burkina Faso* | **80.** *Hawaii*

NEXT
OR TRY AGAIN?

81 Where is Mount Kennedy?

82 What does the Beaufort scale measure?

83 What is the third largest continent in the world?

84 What is Alabama's most popular nickname?

85 What body of water is fed by the Danube River?

86 Name the city planned by French architect Pierre L'Enfant in 1791, also known as Federal City.

87 Is the Tropic of Capricorn north or south of the equator?

88 Name the largest river by discharge volume of water in the world.

89 What is the smallest state in the U.S.?

90 Where is Broadway?

91 What country produces the original Edam cheese?

92 What does Honolulu mean?

93 Name the two continents divided by the Bosporus strait.

94 Why did builders choose International Orange as the color of the Golden Gate Bridge?

95 Where is the biggest volcano in the United States?

96 What's the name of deepest oceanic trench on Earth?

97 What is considered to be the most important island in the United States?

98 Which U.S. national park runs across Montana, Idaho and Wyoming?

99 What is the term for a piece of land surrounded by water?

100 Which American bridge has people who will drive you across if you're afraid to drive yourself?

Answers 81. Yukon | **82.** It measures wind speeds | **83.** North America | **84.** The Heart of Dixie | **85.** Black Sea | **86.** Washington D.C. | **87.** South | **88.** Amazon River (they live in all south American rivers except for Chile) | **89.** Rhode Island | **90.** New York City, USA. | **91.** The Netherlands | **92.** Sheltered harbor | **93.** Europe and Asia | **94.** The color was easy to see through the fog | **95.** Alaska. | **96.** Mariana Trench | **97.** Manhattan | **98.** Yellowstone National Park | **99.** Island | **100.** The Mackinac Bridge over Lake Michigan

WHAT'S THE
BEST TRIVIA
BOOK?

HISTORY TRIVIA

LOUIS RICHARDS

DID YOU KNOW?

THE FIRST WEBCAM EVER WATCHED A COFFEE POT.

HISTORY

1. What favorite toy of the 1980s was associated with Xavier Roberts?

2. Who succeeded Kennedy as president of the United States, hours after his death?

3. 1789 marked the beginning of which revolution?

4. Who was the first democratically elected president of Russia?

5. Who wrote the history of Rome from its origins to the year 9 BC, in 142 books?

6. Which Egyptian president ordered troops to seize the Suez Canal in the mid-1900s?

7. Besides English, which languages did Thomas Jefferson know?

8. What is the name of the winged horse of Greek mythology?

9. In the U.S., how many states did Nixon carry in the 1972 elections?

10. What was the first city to reach a population of one million?

11. Which Egyptian temple was dismantled and rebuilt stone by stone when the Aswan Dam was built?

12. In France, which king was also known as the Sun King?

13. What was the Choctaw Indians' police force called?

14. Which actor died in a car crash on their way to a race?

15. Henry Shrapnel invented what?

16. Which magician was an advisor to King Arthur?

17. Which famous general was once attacked by rabbits?

18. For how many years did the 30 Years War last? 27, 30 or 36?

19. Which empire had no written language?

20. What treaty, signed in 1713, ended the War of the Spanish Succession?

Answers 1. Cabbage Patch Kids | 2. Lyndon B. Johnson | 3. The French Revolution | 4. Boris Yeltsin | 5. Livy (Titus Livius) | 6. President Nasser | 7. French, Greek, Italian, Latin, and Spanish. | 8. Pegasus | 9. Forty-nine | 10. Ancient Rome | 11. Abu Simbel | 12. Louis XIV | 13. Lighthorse | 14. James Dean | 15. The exploding shell | 16. Merlin | 17. Napoleon Bonaparte | 18. 30 Years | 19. The Incan Empire | 20. Treaty of Utrecht

21 When John F Kennedy was assassinated, how old was he?

22 Who invented the famous Revolver gun?

23 Where did the first atomic bomb explode?

24 In early 2011, Donald Trump began to publicly question two things about President Barack Obama; what were they?

25 Pocahontas belonged to which Native American tribe?

26 What is Myrrh?

27 In Qumran, Jordan, what was discovered by a shepherd boy in 1947?

28 What is the more common name for the American M4 tank?

29 A Roman Legion was made up of how many men?

30 When was the Declaration of Independence signed?

31 The U.S. began direct military involvement in Vietnam in what year?

32 In 1803, the land that would come to be known as Oklahoma was part of the what?

33 What were the names of Christopher Columbus' ships?

34 Which U.S. president served as a high rank military officer during World War II?

35 Who is credited with the invention of the first car?

36 Name the U.S. President, Chester Alan _____.

37 The fall of the Berlin Wall happened on November 9 of which year?

38 In 1958, which toy was launched by Danish toymakers Ole and Godtfred Kristiansen?

39 In which year did the United States enter World War I?

40 Which country suffered most deaths in combat during World War II?

Answers 21. 46 | **22.** Samuel Colt | **23.** New Mexico | **24.** Citizenship and eligibility to serve as president. | **25.** Powhatan | **26.** Gum resin, used as a perfume, anointing oil, incense, and medicine | **27.** The Dead Sea Scrolls | **28.** The Sherman tank | **29.** 4000 - 6000 | **30.** August 2, 1776 | **31.** 1965 | **32.** Louisiana purchase. | **33.** The Nina, the Pinta and the Santa Maria | **34.** Dwight D. Eisenhower | **35.** Karl Benz | **36.** Arthur | **37.** 1989 | **38.** Lego | **39.** 1917 | **40.** The USSR (approx. 20 million)

HISTORY

41 Which Belgian noblewoman received a death sentence for bathing in the blood of murdered servant girls to preserve her youth?

42 In which ocean was the Battle of Midway fought?

43 When do archaeologists believe the Rosetta stone was written?

44 How old was Catherine of Aragon when she was betrothed to Prince Arthur?

45 Which ocean was Amelia Earhart flying over when she vanished?

46 What is the name of the greatest "fabulist" of all time?

47 How was the Anglo-Chinese war of 1839-1842 more commonly known?

48 Who did Spartacus fight against in the Third Servile War?

49 Which wife of Henry VIII was accused of adultery, incest and conspiracy and beheaded for it?

50 When did the American civil war end?

51 In which city did Americans famously dump an entire shipment of tea into the harbor?

52 Which famous horse was the winner of the Kentucky Derby in 1973?

53 Name the earliest system of laws.

54 What ancient Greek city was the original host of the Olympic Games?

55 Roman statues were made with a certain detachable body part, so that one could be removed and replaced by another. What was it?

56 The biggest German warship of WWII was named after which famous chancellor?

57 What Roman emperor was killed on March 15, 44 BC by a group of senators?

58 Which famous U.S. author published President Grant's autobiography?

59 In Medieval times what was the name given to an area controlled by a lord?

60 What Soviet satellite was the first to be launched into space in 1957?

Answers 41. Countess Elizabeth Bathory | 42. Pacific Ocean | 43. 196 BC, in Memphis, Egypt | 44. She was three | 45. Atlantic Ocean | 46. Aesop | 47. The Opium War | 48. The Roman Republic | 49. Anne Boleyn | 50. May 9, 1865 | 51. Boston | 52. Secretariat | 53. Code of Hammurabi | 54. Olympia | 55. The Head | 56. Bismarck | 57. Julius Caesar | 58. Mark Twain | 59. Feud | 60. Sputnik

HOW
DO YOU
FEEL?

61 Fort Sumter and Shiloh are famous battles of which war?

62 Which international body was established in 1945, following World War II?

63 What was the name of the famous route taken by the Cherokee Indians to Oklahoma during their relocation?

64 Who is considered to be "the father of history"?

65 In what year did Napoleon Bonaparte's reign as Emperor of France begin?

66 The Statue of Liberty was actually a gift from which European country?

67 In 1955, what reference book went on sale for the first time?

68 Which U.S. president was the first to live in the White House?

69 What was the name of the ancient emperor married to Roxana?

70 200,000 British troops fled from which French port on June 4th 1940?

71 Name the temple in Athens Acropolis dedicated to the goddess Athena.

72 When was the storming of the Bastille?

73 Where in France did Joan of Arc die?

74 Who designed the White House?

75 During the classical era, which word was used to describe all foreigners who lacked Greek and Roman traditions?

76 This Native American tribe was the first to encounter the pilgrims.

77 In which century was The War of the Roses fought?

78 Which German city received the heaviest bombing of WWII in early 1945?

79 What relation was Louis XV to his predecessor, Louis XIV of France?

80 Little Boy' and 'Fat Man' were names for what?

79. Great-grandson | 80. Atomic Bombs
74. James Hoban | 75. Barbarians | 76. Nauset tribe | 77. 15th Century | 78. Dresden |
69. Alexander the Great | 70. Dunkirk | 71. Parthenon | 72. July 14, 1789 | 73. Rouen |
64. Herodotus | 65. 1804 | 66. France | 67. Guinness Book Of Records | 68. John Adams |
Answers 61. American Civil War | 62. The United Nations | 63. The Trail of Tears |

NEXT
OR TRY AGAIN?

HISTORY

81 Who was the last tsar of Russia?

82 Sir Howard Carter discovered what in 1922?

83 What was the original name for the presidential retreat, Camp David?

84 What was the name of the place also known as the 'Isle of Apples', where Christ and Joseph of Arimathea are supposed to have travelled?

85 What was the first American state?

86 What is considered to be the deadliest battle in American history?

87 How many people were killed in the Salem Witch Trials?

88 Who served as chief minister to King Henry VIII of England?

89 What process is used for dating ancient organic objects?

90 Which famous serial killer was less-commonly known as the Whitechapel Murderer?

91 Who was the Roman Emperor blamed for The Great Fire of Rome?

92 Who was the main force behind France's Reign of Terror?

93 What important event in human history happened on July 20, 1969 for the first time?

94 How many British colonies formed the United States?

95 Who made the first non-stop transatlantic crossing in an airplane?

96 Who was the first ruler of the Mongol Empire?

97 In New York City, on May 1st 1931, the world's tallest building (at the time) was opened. What was it called?

98 In 1955, who made headlines after refusing to give up her seat to a white person?

99 A Ballista was a type of what?

100 What was the first English settlement in America?

Answers 81. Nicholas II | **82.** Tutankhamun's Tomb | **83.** Shangri-La | **84.** Avalon | **85.** Delaware | **86.** The Battle of Antietam | **87.** Twenty-five (20 people executed for witchcraft and 5 died in jail) | **88.** Thomas Cromwell | **89.** Radiocarbon Dating | **90.** Jack the Ripper | **91.** Nero | **92.** Robespierre | **93.** The Lunar Landing Mission | **94.** Thirteen | **95.** Charles A. Lindbergh | **96.** Genghis Khan | **97.** Empire State Building | **98.** Rosa Parks | **99.** An ancient siege machine, a giant catapult or crossbow | **100.** Jamestown, Virginia

WHAT'S THE
BEST TRIVIA
BOOK?

PEOPLE & PLACES
TRIVIA

DID YOU KNOW?

THE LONGEST MOUSTACHE EVER IS 4.29M (14FT) LONG AND BELONGS TO AN INDIAN MAN.

PEOPLE & PLACES

1. What is the name of Fidel Castro's brother?

2. Who were Balthazar, Melchior and Gaspar?

3. Which celebrity launched a perfume line called 'M' for Christmas?

4. The Friday after Thanksgiving in the United States is commonly known as?

5. Where did the world's first Starbucks open?

6. Who was the Captain of the Titanic when it sank?

7. Tea, the third most consumed beverage in the world, originates from which Asian country?

8. Which German city is considered the world capital of beer?

9. In which country is Johannesburg located?

10. In 1979, which famous Egyptian businessman bought Paris' Ritz Hotel?

11. Who did Lee Harvey Oswald kill?

12. Who was the first female Prime Minister of the United Kingdom?

13. Who was the first American chess champion?

14. Which King is famous for supposedly trying to turn back the sea?

15. Who was the first to die from King Tut's curse?

16. Which U.S. president had fake dentures made from the teeth of slaves?

17. In which country is the city and port of Antwerp located?

18. Which city was the first capital of the United States?

19. Name the founder of Playboy magazine.

20. The Dead Sea can be found in these two countries.

Answers 1. Raul | 2. The 3 Wise Men | 3. Mariah Carey | 4. Black Friday | 5. Seattle | 6. Captain Edward J. Smith | 7. China | 8. Munich | 9. Russia | 10. Mohammed Al-Fayed | 11. John F. Kennedy | 12. Margaret Thatcher | 13. Bobby Fischer | 14. King Canute | 15. Lord Carnarvon (The financial backer of the excavation) | 16. George Washington | 17. Belgium | 18. New York City | 19. Hugh Hefner | 20. Israel and Jordan

21 Who wrote the fictional novel Frankenstein?

22 Which U.S. president has won two Grammy awards?

23 Who was the author of "The Witching Hour"?

24 What's the oldest university in the United States?

25 Which American actress truly found her charming prince in 1956?

26 What was the name of the German who landed his plane in Red Square?

27 Whose real name is "Cherilyn Sarkisian La Pierre"?

28 Who ran against Reagan in 1984 and lost?

29 Vanilla is originally from which country?

30 What was the first state in the United States to legalize marijuana for medicinal use?

31 Of what nationality was Hans Christian Andersen?

32 Which U.S. president spent the shortest time in office?

33 Who was the first woman appointed to the U.S. Supreme Court?

34 What name is Allan Stewart Konigsberg more commonly known as?

35 In which U.S. state can you find the Liberty Bell?

36 Name the person who led the Million Man March on Washington.

37 Who was killed by Indians at the battle of Little Bighorn?

38 Whose birth name is Farouk Bulsara?

39 In which cities of the United States were the Kennedy brothers assassinated?

40 What is the tallest building in the United States and where is it?

Answers 21. Mary Shelley | 22. Bill Clinton | 23. Anne Rice | 24. Harvard | 25. Grace Kelly | 26. Mathias Rust | 27. Cher | 28. Walter Mondale | 29. Mexico (originally called tlixochitl, meaning "black flower") | 30. California (1996) | 31. Danish | 32. William Henry Harrison | 33. Sandra Day O'Connor (1981) | 34. Woody Allen | 35. Pennsylvania | 36. Louis Farrakhan | 37. General George Armstrong Custer | 38. Freddie Mercury | 39. Dallas, Texas (John) and Los Angeles, California (Robert) | 40. One World Trade Center in New York City

PEOPLE & PLACES

HOW DO YOU FEEL?

41 Who became president following the assassination of Abraham Lincoln?

42 Where was Mike Tyson born?

43 What were the Titanic's sister ships called?

44 Name the first Catholic president of the United States.

45 Who was the first and only person to hold both the titles of Vice President and President of the United States?

46 What was the name of New Orleans' 2005 devastating hurricane?

47 What year did the first Apple retail store open?

48 The First Lady of the United States to win an Emmy Award was…

49 The United States bought Alaska from which country?

50 What is Bob Dylan's real name?

51 Which U.S. president worked as a lifeguard?

52 What were the 1920s called in the United States?

53 Which U.S. president was previously a peanut farmer?

54 Who was Molly Pitcher?

55 Who was the third wife of King Henry VIII?

56 Who was the first woman to officially become a billionaire in the U.S.?

57 Whose U.S. Election campaign slogan was "You've Never Had It So Good"?

58 Which four presidents are depicted on Mount Rushmore?

59 When Uncle Sam first got a beard, who was president of the U.S?

60 Who was awarded with the only Nobel Peace Prize given during WWI?

Answers 41. Andrew Johnson | 42. Brooklyn, New York | 43. Olympic and Britannic | 44. John F. Kennedy | 45. Gerald Ford | 46. Hurricane Katrina | 47. 2001 | 48. Jacqueline Kennedy | 49. Russia | 50. Robert Zimmerman | 51. Ronald Reagan | 52. The Roaring Twenties | 53. Jimmy Carter | 54. A woman said to have fought in the American Revolutionary War | 55. Jane Seymour | 56. Martha Stewart | 57. Harold Macmillan, 1959 | 58. Theodore Roosevelt, George Washington, Abraham Lincoln and Thomas Jefferson | 59. Abraham Lincoln | 60. The International Red Cross

PEOPLE & PLACES

61 Who was the first female U.S. astronaut?

62 Who led the Alamo attack?

63 What is the postal address of the White House?

64 What was Jacqueline Kennedy's maiden name?

65 Who was the first U.S. president to be impeached?

66 Who was the last Apache warrior chief?

67 Who is famous for playing bowls before engaging The Spanish Armada?

68 Who bought one of Leonardo Da Vinci's notebooks in 1994 for more than 19 million British pounds?

69 Three of Santa's reindeers' names begin with D., Dasher, Dancer and?

70 Who was the German Officer who rescued Mussolini and lived and died in Madrid?

71 Who was the second man to walk on the moon?

72 Which candidate did the LA times endorse in the 1964 U.S. presidential election?

73 From what did Al Capone died?

74 Who was convicted for masterminding the Helter Skelter murders?

75 Who did Pocahontas marry?

76 What establishments have no windows or clocks?

77 Who created the fifty-star pattern on the United States flag?

78 Who was Ronald Regan's first wife?

79 What is the name of the world's largest coral reef system?

80 What is the Donner Party known for?

Answers 61. Sally K. Ride | **62.** Santa Anna | **63.** 1600 Pennsylvania Avenue | **64.** Jacqueline Bouvier | **65.** Andrew Johnson | **66.** Geronimo | **67.** Sir Francis Drake | **68.** Bill Gates | **69.** Donner | **70.** Otto Skorzeny | **71.** Buzz Aldrin | **72.** Barry Goldwater | **73.** Cardiac arrest, he also had Syphilis | **74.** Charles Manson | **75.** John Rolfe | **76.** Casinos | **77.** Robert G. Heft | **78.** Jane Wyman | **79.** The Great Barrier Reef | **80.** Pioneer group trapped in the U.S. Sierra Nevada. Resorted to cannibalism.

PEOPLE & PLACES

81 Which aviator was Time's first Man of the Year?

82 Who was the first black woman elected to the U.S. Congress?

83 What year did the California Gold Rush start?

84 Who invented food-freezing?

85 Who denounced Stalin?

86 While in prison, who did Hitler dictate Mein Kampf to?

87 Where is the Sistine Chapel?

88 Who was in charge of Hitler's Ministry of Propaganda?

89 What was Princess Diana's family name before marrying Prince Charles?

90 Who was the first woman to hold federal executive office in the United States?

91 Which 16th century seer was famous for his predictions?

92 When did the first birth control clinic in the U.S. open?

93 What is the most populated state in the U.S.?

94 What is Barbie doll's full name?

95 Who was the first Christian Emperor of Rome?

96 Washington was a commander who emphasized what above all?

97 Where are the Sinhalese people from?

98 Where is the only place in the U.S. where you can stand in four states at once?

99 Who did John Wilkes Booth assassinate?

100 Which U.S. city was the site of a major fire in 1871?

Answers 81. Charles Lindbergh | 82. Shirley Chisholm | 83. 1848 | 84. Clarence Birdseye | 85. Nikita Khrushchev | 86. Rudolf Hess | 87. Vatican City | 88. Joseph Goebbels | 89. Spencer | 90. Kamala Harris | 91. Nostradamus | 92. 1916 | 93. California | 94. Barbara Millicent Roberts | 95. Constantine | 96. Training | 97. Sri Lanka | 98. Four Corners | 99. Abraham Lincoln | 100. Chicago

WHAT'S THE
BEST TRIVIA
BOOK?

RELIGION
& MYTHOLOGY
TRIVIA

DID YOU KNOW?

THE YOUNGEST POPE WAS ONLY 11 YEARS OLD.

RELIGION & MYTHOLOGY

1. What is Islam's holy book?

2. The oldest route to Santiago de Compostela, first taken in the 9th century, is referred to as the Original Way or Camino Primitivo, and begins where?

3. Which religion uses the Avesta texts?

4. Shintoism is associated with what country?

5. If travelling the Way of St. James pilgrimage on a bike, what distance needs to be travelled to receive a certificate of accomplishment?

6. What is the name of a Muslim male's yearly pilgrimage to Mecca?

7. What is the 1st book of the Hindu scripture?

8. Who is the Roman equivalent of the Greek god Ares?

9. Who killed a dragon in the 12th century, in ancient mythology?

10. Which religion worships Vishnu and Brahma?

11. In theology, the study of final things such as death, judgment and the end of the world is called what?

12. In Greek mythology, who was the son of Peleus and Thetis?

13. What Chinese religion was founded by Laozi or Lao Tzu?

14. Which book of the Bible was written by King David?

15. What are the 7 Deadly Sins?

16. For Muslims, Muhammad is a prophet. What is Jesus for them?

17. Whose teaching consisted of four 'Noble Truths'?

18. Who was the ancient Egyptian sun god?

19. Which Roman soldier pierced the crucified Christ with his spear?

20. Shia or Shi'ite is a term used to denote a branch of which major religion?

Answers 1. Koran | 2. Oviedo | 3. Zoroastrianism | 4. Japan | 5. 200km (124 miles) | 6. Hajj | 7. Rig Veda | 8. Mars | 9. St. George | 10. Hinduism | 11. Eschatology | 12. Achilles | 13. Taoism | 14. Psalms | 15. Pride, greed, lust, envy, gluttony, wrath and sloth. | 16. A prophet and a messenger | 17. Buddha | 18. Ra | 19. Longinus | 20. Islam

21 Which two books in the Old Testament list the Ten Commandments? (In order of appearance)?

22 What day has the Catholic Church determined to be the day Christ rose from the dead?

23 Who led the Mormons to Utah?

24 What is Islam's holy month called?

25 According to the Bible, who were the brothers of Jesus?

26 How many animals of each kind did Moses take onto the ark?

27 In what city does a certain church forbid burping or sneezing?

28 In Greek mythology who did Athena turn into a spider?

29 Who is the Greek god of war?

30 What religion is Joseph Smith associated with?

31 How many Popes have been of Spanish origin?

32 How long did it take God to create the Universe?

33 Where was Mother Theresa born?

34 According to the Bible, how many years did Jesus live?

35 What has no reflection, no shadow, and can't stand the smell of garlic?

36 Who was the father of Zeus?

37 What is the name of the Hindu festival of lights?

38 Which religious group produces the magazine The Watchtower?

39 Where was Methodism founded?

40 How many Pillars does Islam have?

Answers 21. Exodus and Deuteronomy | 22. Easter Sunday | 23. Brigham Young | 24. Ramadan | 25. James, Joseph, Judas/Jude and Simon | 26. None (it was Noah, not Moses) | 27. Omaha, Nebraska | 28. Arachne | 29. Ares | 30. Mormonism and the Latter Day Saint movement | 31. Two – Pope Alexander VI and Pope Callixtus III | 32. Six days - he rested on the seventh | 33. Republic of Macedonia | 34. 33 | 35. Vampires | 36. Cronus | 37. Diwali (or Deepavali) | 38. Jehovah's Witnesses | 39. United Kingdom | 40. Five

RELIGION & MYTHOLOGY

41 The "Harmandir Sahib" or Golden Temple belongs to which religion?

42 Which Roman God was the equivalent of the Greek God Dionysus?

43 What belief system does the Dalai Lama hold?

44 Geographically, where did Protestantism originate?

45 How old is a Jewish boy when he becomes a man?

46 In Egyptian mythology, who is known as the god of the desert?

47 Name the German priest who started the Protestant Reformation.

48 Part of what mollusk is generally regarded as a symbol of the Camino de Santiago?

49 Which Greek God was the equivalent of the Roman God Mercury?

50 In what country is the Islamic holy city of Mecca?

51 Apollo was the Greek god of?

52 Protestants call their priests by these two terms.

53 Who was the Ancient Egyptian goddess of fertility, love and beauty?

54 Who is the Roman goddess of luck?

55 What is the date of St. Patrick's Day?

56 What two biblical cities did God destroy with fire and brimstone?

57 Candomblé is an African religion, widely popular in which South American country?

58 In Greek mythology who became the queen of the Underworld after being abducted by Hades?

59 What did Pandora release when she opened the box?

60 Which Norse God has a hammer called Mjolnir?

Answers 41. Sikhism | 42. Bacchus | 43. Buddhist | 44. Germany | 45. Thirteen | 46. Seth | 47. Martin Luther | 48. Scallop | 49. Hermes | 50. Saudi Arabia | 51. Sun, music, poetry, prophecy, and medicine | 52. Reverend and pastor | 53. Hathor | 54. Fortuna | 55. March 17 | 56. Sodom and Gomorrah | 57. Brazil | 58. Persephone | 59. Misery and evil | 60. Thor

61 Ancient Egyptian goddess worshiped in the form of a lioness or cat.

62 What book is the holiest for devout Jews?

63 What religion has the most global followers?

64 Name of the Aztec God of rain.

65 The goal of all Buddhists is to be free from all suffering, which is known as?

66 In Norse mythology, where is the home of the gods?

67 Where did Taoism originate?

68 What religion was founded by Zarathustra?

69 In 1985, the route of the Way of St. James pilgrimage was named one of UNESCO's what?

70 Where is the Pilgrim's Mass held daily?

71 Who killed Medusa?

72 What is the name given to the supreme deity in Hinduism?

73 In China why were kites flown on the ninth day of every month?

74 Where did the Bahai religion originate?

75 Which ancient continent is said to be submerged?

76 What was the first sign shown to Moses by God according to the Bible?

77 When a female Sikh is baptized, she receives the surname Kaur, what does it mean in English?

78 What was the town that ancient Greeks believed to be the center of the world, and was the home of a famous oracle?

79 The Valkyries are the nine handmaidens of whom?

80 In Hawaiian religion who is the goddess of volcanoes and creator of the Hawaiian Islands?

Answers 61. Bastet | 62. The Torah | 63. Christianity | 64. Tlaloc | 65. Nirvana | 66. Asgard | 67. China | 68. Zoroastrianism | 69. World Heritage Sites | 70. Cathedral of Santiago de Compostela | 71. Perseus | 72. Shiva | 73. To banish evil | 74. Iran | 75. Atlantis | 76. A burning bush | 77. Princess | 78. Delphi | 79. Odin | 80. Pele

RELIGION & MYTHOLOGY

81 In Greek mythology who are the incarnations of destiny?

82 What is the name of a Jewish temple?

83 Who was the first Pope?

84 How many Archangels are there?

85 According to the Bible who was saved from drowning when he was swallowed by a whale?

86 Which country has the largest Muslim population?

87 The souls of Norse warriors killed in battle went to which place?

88 In which modern day city of the world did the Aztecs live?

89 In Greek mythology which Titan was condemned to carry the world on his shoulders?

90 Who was the Roman goddess equivalent to Venus?

91 On which mountain did God give Moses the Ten Commandments?

92 Which country has the largest Buddhist population?

93 What is a Buddhist temple called?

94 According to the Book of Genesis what happened when God said "fiat lux"?

95 Freyja is the Norse goddess of?

96 What is the name of the elephant-headed Hindu god?

97 What is the sacred city for all Christians, Jews and Muslims?

98 Who was the "Mother goddess" of Egypt?

99 Loki is the Norse god of what?

100 What are Muslim temples called?

Answers 81. Moirai or Fates | **82.** Synagogue | **83.** Peter | **84.** Seven | **85.** Jonah | **86.** Indonesia | **87.** Valhalla | **88.** Mexico City | **89.** Atlas | **90.** Aphrodite | **91.** Mount Sinai | **92.** Cambodia | **93.** Pagoda | **94.** Light appeared ("Let there be light") | **95.** Love, beauty, fertility | **96.** Ganesh | **97.** Jerusalem | **98.** Isis | **99.** Mischief | **100.** Mosques

WHAT'S THE
BEST TRIVIA
BOOK?

HOLIDAYS TRIVIA

DID YOU KNOW?

Titanic crew had no binoculars. They were inside a locker and the key was lost.

HOLIDAYS

1. Who was the first ghost to appear to Scrooge in the Dickens classic A Christmas Carol?

2. In which country of the world is the most famous and crowded carnival held?

3. Which month has no holidays in the U.S.?

4. Which U.S. president was the first to have a Christmas tree in the White House?

5. Which American president is commemorated on National Freedom Day?

6. Halloween originated from a festival celebrated by which ancient European tribe?

7. What was the name of that festival?

8. Presidents' Day is also officially which president's birthday?

9. By what name is St Sylvester's Day otherwise known?

10. In the UK, what day is also known as "Stir-Up Sunday"?

11. What is the name of the famous Pennsylvania groundhog?

12. When was the term Xmas invented?

13. What is the connection between "Comet," "Cupid" and "Vixen"?

14. What Christian holiday is celebrated immediately after Halloween?

15. When was the date of the Christian festival Easter fixed by the Council of Nicaea?

16. What does holly symbolize at Christmas?

17. Which U. S. president disregarded health and safety and insisted on putting lit candles on the White House Christmas tree?

18. All Saints' Day is famously celebrated in Mexico as _____.

19. Which reindeer isn't featured in the poem The Night before Christmas?

20. As of 2022, what is the most recently designated federal holiday in the U.S.?

Answers 1. Marley's Ghost | 2. Brazil | 3. August | 4. Benjamin Harrison | 5. Abraham Lincoln | 6. The Celts | 7. Samhain | 8. George Washington | 9. New Year's Eve | 10. The last Sunday before Advent | 11. Punxsutawney Phil | 12. Around 1500's | 13. All names of Santa's reindeer | 14. All Saints Day | 15. 325 AD | 16. The crown of thorns worn by Jesus | 17. Franklin D. Roosevelt | 18. Day of the Dead | 19. Rudolph | 20. Juneteenth (June 19)

HOW DO YOU FEEL?™

START

HOLIDAYS

WHAT'S THE
BEST TRIVIA
BOOK?

32

21 Which animal is the symbol of Easter?

22 What do you do with Swedish glogg?

23 What is the link between Justin Trudeau, Ryan Seacrest and Isaac Newton?

24 What was given on the eighth day of Christmas?

25 Where did the tradition of Christmas trees originate?

26 When is Boxing Day celebrated?

27 In China, the Chinese New Year is also known as?

28 What are the two U.S. presidents officially celebrated on Presidents' Day?

29 When is the "Feast of Stephen"?

30 What was called Armistice Day in the U.S. until 1954?

31 What gift was given on the first day of Christmas?

32 Which American tycoon was born on Christmas Day and created one of the world's biggest hotel chains?

33 In which year was the first New Year's Eve ball drop?

34 Which date marks the Christian Epiphany, when Jesus, Mary and Joseph met the Three Wise Men?

35 Which American musician nicknamed the Godfather of Soul died on Christmas day?

36 When is Presidents' Day celebrated?

37 What famous city in the U.S. dyes its river green for St. Patrick's Day?

38 What is the name for the Jewish New Year?

39 What is the U.S. equivalent of Remembrance Day in the UK?

40 FINISH What is the name of the lamp lit during the Jewish holiday of Hanukkah?

Answers 21. Bunny | 22. Drink it, it's a hot spiced drink made from wine or spirits | 23. Born On Christmas Day | 24. Eight Maids-a-milking | 25. Germany (5th Century) | 26. December 26th | 27. Spring Festival | 28. George Washington and Abraham Lincoln | 29. December 26th | 30. Veterans Day | 31. A Partridge in a Pear Tree | 32. Conrad Hilton | 33. 1907 | 34. January 6th | 35. James Brown | 36. The third Monday in February | 37. Chicago | 38. Rosh Hashanah | 39. Veterans Day | 40. Menorah

HOLIDAYS

41 Which 3 singers have sung the opening line to "Do They Know It's Christmas"?

42 Why is the 26th of December known as Boxing Day?

43 True or false, Hannukah falls on the same day every year.

44 Which popular Christmas song has been a hit in four different decades?

45 According to some legends, which festive decoration is attributed to spiders?

46 Which native Mexican flower is also known as the Christmas flower?

47 Where does Saint Nicholas come from?

48 Which U.S. president moved Thanksgiving's date to lengthen the holiday shopping season?

49 What does the word Hanukkah mean?

50 From what phrase does the word Halloween come from?

51 The popular Hindu Festival of Colors is called ____.

52 When is the Feast of St. Nicholas? Dec 6th, Dec 18th, Dec 25th, or Dec 27th?

53 On what day do children in Italy and Spain traditionally get their Christmas presents?

54 On November 5th, people of England celebrate which holiday?

55 What is the name of St. Patrick's famous symbol?

56 In which country is Kwanzaa celebrated?

57 What seasonal name was given to Bart Simpson's dog?

58 Which city is known as "The Gingerbread Capital of the World"?

59 The Day of the Dead is considered a celebration of life, not death. Yes or no?

60 Which country invented the "Christmas Cracker"?

Answers 41. Paul Young, Kylie Minogue, Chris Martin | 42. The rich gave presents to the poor, the masters gave presents to the servant | 43. False | 44. Mariah Carey's All I Want For Christmas is You | 45. Tinsel | 46. The poinsettia | 47. Turkey | 48. Franklin D. Roosevelt | 49. Dedication | 50. All Hallows Eve | 51. Holi | 52. Dec 6th | 53. January 5th | 54. Guy Fawkes Day | 55. Shamrock | 56. It's primarily an African American holiday | 57. Santa's Little Helper | 58. Nuremberg | 59. Yes | 60. England

HOW DO YOU FEEL?

61 What flowers are known as the Day of the Dead Flowers?

62 What were the Three Wise Men's gifts?

63 Which river did George Washington cross on Christmas night in 1776 during the American Revolutionary War?

64 The Jewish Festival of Lights is also commonly known as?

65 How many federal holidays does the U.S. have?

66 When was D-day?

67 Black Independence Day in the U.S. is also known as what?

68 Is St. Patrick Ireland's patron saint? Yes or no?

69 What holiday became popular after it was featured on the TV show Seinfeld?

70 Complete the verse – "'Twas the night before Christmas, when all through the house, not a creature was stirring not even a ____."

71 What did Rudolph the Red-nosed Reindeer never get to join in?

72 Who are the three ghosts in Charles Dickens' novel A Christmas Carol?

73 When is Martin Luther King Jr. Day celebrated?

74 In the U.S., who is honored on Memorial Day?

75 What is the name of the female skull symbol of The Day of the Dead?

76 Presepe in Italian refers to which Christmas tradition?

77 What is the name of the famous Christmas tree in New York City?

78 By what name was the American comedian and actor William Claude, who died on Christmas day, better known?

79 On which date is Epiphany celebrated in the traditional Western calendar?

80 Name the former dictator executed by firing squad on Christmas Day of 1999.

Answers 61. Marigolds | 62. Gold, frankincense and myrrh | 63. Delaware | 64. Hanukkah | 65. Eleven | 66. June 6th, 1944 | 67. Juneteenth | 68. Yes | 69. Festivus | 70. Mouse | 71. Any reindeer games | 72. Christmas Past, Present and Future | 73. Third Monday of January | 74. United States' military personnel who have died in service | 75. Catrina | 76. Nativity scene (literally meaning crib) | 77. Rockefeller Tree | 78. WC Fields | 79. 6th January | 80. Nicolae Ceausescu

NEXT OR TRY AGAIN?

35

WHAT'S THE
**BEST TRIVIA
BOOK?**

HOW
DO YOU
FEEL?

HOLIDAYS

81 What is the next line in the song after "I'm dreaming of a white Christmas"?

82 Name the Jewish festival commemorating the recovery of Jerusalem.

83 Michael Myers is the serial killer in which series of films?

84 When is Kwanzaa celebrated?

85 What is celebrated on Juneteenth or Black Independence Day?

86 Which American holiday celebrates the giving of thanks for the autumn harvest?

87 Hanukkah is celebrated for how many nights?

88 Which president made the turkey pardon tradition official?

89 Halloween is celebrated on the eve of which Christian holiday?

90 What U.S. holiday is celebrated on the first Monday in September?

91 What U.S. holiday celebrates and honors indigenous cultures in the United States and the Americas?

92 Women's History Month is celebrated during which month?

93 The song "Jingle Bells" is thought to have been originally written for which other holiday?

94 Which holiday was banned for several years by the Puritans in the United States?

95 What is the name of Kwanzaa's candle holder?

LOUIS RICHARDS

WHAT'S THE
BEST TRIVIA
BOOK?

ART & LITERATURE
TRIVIA

DID YOU KNOW?

ZEBRAS ARE
ACTUALLY BLACK WITH WHITE STRIPES,
NOT WHITE WITH BLACK STRIPES.

ART & LITERATURE

1 Which author described World War One as the War to End All Wars?

2 Which scientist wrote the famous book A Brief History Of Time in 1988?

3 Which American artist became famous in the 1960s for painting iconic American objects?

4 Which European movement between 1800 and 1890 focused on expression and emotion rather than reason?

5 Bram Stoker created which famous character?

6 Who wrote the novel The Silence of the Lambs?

7 Atticus Finch is one of the main characters of which novel?

8 Which American novel was most influential in the abolition of slavery in the U.S.?

9 Which famous book begins with the line "Marley was dead, to begin with. There was no doubt about that"?

10 What do fables teach?

11 Which author created the character of Tarzan?

12 Leonardo da Vinci's Mona Lisa can be found on display in which museum?

13 Who wrote the novel A Farewell to Arms?

14 Name the author of Robinson Crusoe.

15 What is the term for a painting or drawing executed in a single color?

16 In which country was Frida Kahlo born?

17 Who wrote The Bell Jar?

18 The 1925 short story collection, In Our Time, was written by whom?

19 Douglas Adams is most famous for which book?

20 Which artist painted The Kiss?

21 What was the sequel to Louisa May Alcott's Little Women?

22 What famous novel covers only one day, and is set in Dublin in June, 1904?

23 Who painted the Garden of Earthly Delights?

24 What is a term that describes an early 1900s movement in France to explore the unconscious mind?

25 How many lines are there in a sonnet?

26 Duke Leto Atreides and The Harkonnens are characters in what popular sci-fi novel?

27 Name a form of short poetry originally from Japan.

28 Who is the author of the Harry Potter series?

29 What artistic movement began in the 1950s and played with optical patterns?

30 Scheherazade is a story teller in which literary work?

31 Which science fiction story centers on alien children in a village?

32 What is the term for a 19th-century art movement that refers to objective or realistic representation?

33 What is the title of Homer's account of the Trojan War?

34 Hercule Poirot is a fictional Belgian detective created by which famous writer?

35 Who wrote Of Mice and Men, The Grapes of Wrath and East of Eden?

36 Which Mary Shelley novel is considered to have defined the form of science-fiction novels?

37 What is the name of the American neo-classical architectural style created by Thomas Jefferson?

38 In A Christmas Carol, what was the name of the main character?

39 Found in New York City, what does MoMa stand for?

40 What recent artistic movement emphasizes the idea of art over the art itself?

Answers 21. Little Men | 22. Ulysses By James Joyce | 23. Hieronymus Bosch | 24. Surrealism | 25. 14 | 26. Dune | 27. Haiku | 28. J.K. Rowling | 29. Op Art | 30. The Arabian Nights / The One Thousand and One Nights | 31. The Midwich Cuckoos | 32. Realism | 33. Iliad | 34. Agatha Christie | 35. John Steinbeck | 36. Frankenstein | 37. Jeffersonian | 38. Ebenezer Scrooge | 39. Modern Museum of Art | 40. Conceptual art

NEXT
OR TRY AGAIN?
61

ART & LITERATURE

41 What is the term for cutting into a solid material to make a sculpture?

42 What novel features the firemen burning books?

43 The three main types of Greek columns are Doric, Ionic, and?

44 How many lines form a Haiku?

45 In Wuthering Heights, what is Cathy's last name?

46 The famous 17th century painting by Johannes Vermeer is called The Girl With a _____ what?

47 Name the author of The Catcher in the Rye.

48 Rembrandt van Rijn famously painted The Militia Company of Captain Frans Banning Cocq, by what name is it better known?

49 Who created the famous detective Sherlock Holmes?

50 What is the name of the bird in the Peanuts comic strip?

51 Who wrote Psycho?

52 What is the name of the monster in Mary Shelley's novel Frankenstein?

53 What do you call a picture that is made of various materials stuck together?

54 The technique of producing printed designs through various methods of incising on wood or metal blocks, which are then inked and printed.

55 Name the French impressionist Claude?

56 The technique of painting with small dots of color.

57 The famous sculpture The Thinker was made by whom?

58 What is the name for ground chalk or plaster mixed with glue, used as a base coat for tempera and oil painting?

59 What is the name of the green layer formed on the surface of copper, brass and bronze sculptures due to oxidation?

60 Name the Mexican painter best known for her self-portraits.

Answers 41. Carving | **42.** Fahrenheit 451 | **43.** Corinthian | **44.** Three | **45.** Earnshaw | **46.** Pearl Earring | **47.** J.D. Salinger | **48.** The Night Watch | **49.** Sir Arthur Conan Doyle | **50.** Woodstock | **51.** Robert Bloch | **52.** He doesn't have a name | **53.** A collage | **54.** Engraving | **55.** Monet | **56.** Pointillism | **57.** Auguste Rodin | **58.** Gesso | **59.** Patina | **60.** Frida Kahlo

61 What does JK of JK Rowling stand for?

62 Who wrote The Sound & The Fury, and As I Lay Dying?

63 A flat board used by a painter to mix and hold colors is known as a what?

64 Baroque Art was a movement supported and encouraged by which religion?

65 Name the decorative style popular in the 1920s & 1930s and found in the Empire State Building.

66 Who painted American Gothic, depicting a farmer standing beside his daughter?

67 What American painting and sculpting movement emphasized strict, systematic compositions?

68 Which Sherlock Holmes novel was most famous?

69 What is an Onomatopoeia?

70 Who wrote The Da Vinci Code?

71 Who wrote the horror novels Carrie and Pet Sematary?

72 Lolita is a famous yet controversial novel by Russian author Vladimir Nabokov, written in which language?

73 What is the name for water-soluble paint made from pigments and a plastic binder?

74 La Gioconda is better known as?

75 Name the group of American painters who united to oppose academic and aesthetic standards in the early 20th century?

76 The Scream was created by which artist?

77 What is the term for choice and arrangement of words and phrases or vocabulary, in a literary work?

78 Name the #1 best-selling book of all time?

79 Name the literary generation who influenced the American post-war era by writing about the rejection of economic materialism, drugs and sexual liberation.

80 Spinning on one foot is known as a what in ballet?

Answers 61. Joanne Kathleen | 62. William Faulkner | 63. Palette | 64. Catholicism | 65. Art Deco | 66. Grant Wood | 67. Minimalism | 68. The Hound of The Baskervilles | 69. The use of words which sound like the event they describe, such as a bang | 70. Dan Brown | 71. Stephen King | 72. English | 73. Acrylic | 74. The Mona Lisa | 75. The Eight | 76. Edvard Munch | 77. Diction | 78. The Bible | 79. The Beat Generation | 80. A Pirouette

ART & LITERATURE

HOW DO YOU FEEL?

81 Odysseus, Homer's main character in The Odyssey is also known as?

82 Name the artistic movement in 19th century U.S. best known for portraying scenes of daily life in New York.

83 An artwork humorously exaggerating the qualities, defects, or peculiarities of a person or idea is called a what?

84 From whom did Bilbo obtain The One Ring?

85 What is the name given to the painting medium involving egg yolks?

86 Who wrote the vampire series that featured Lestat as the main character?

87 Whose 1938 radio reading of The War of The Worlds caused panic in the United States?

88 Who wrote The Adventures of Huckleberry Finn?

89 Which book begins with the famous line: "On January 6, 1482, the people of Paris were awakened by the tumultuous clanging of all the bells in the city"?

90 Frodo is chosen to deliver The One Ring into the heart of what?

91 What famous novel written by Victor Hugo depicts France's social injustice during the 19th century?

92 Which literary character had a dog called Bull's Eye?

93 Who wrote the novel The Narrative of Arthur Gordon Pym of Nantucket?

94 Which character created by Dodie Smith drove a black & white car & wore a black & white fur coat?

95 Ernest Hemingway, F. Scott Fitzgerald and T.S. Eliot are all part of which literary generation?

96 Beth, Jo, Amy and Meg March are all characters created by which novelist?

97 Set in New York's Jazz Age, which novel depicts the story of a famous billionaire and his lover Daisy Buchanan?

98 Name the American literary classic best known for its colorful descriptions of people and places along the Mississippi River.

99 Who painted The Last Supper?

100 The Brothers Karamazov is one of the most famous novels by which Russian author?

Answers 81. Ulysses | **82.** Ash Can School or Ashcan School | **83.** Caricature | **84.** Gollum | **85.** Tempera | **86.** Anne Rice | **87.** Orson Welles | **88.** Mark Twain | **89.** The Hunchback Of Notre Dame | **90.** Mount Doom | **91.** Les Misérables | **92.** Oliver Twist | **93.** Edgar Allan Poe | **94.** Cruella De Vil | **95.** The Lost Generation | **96.** Louisa May Alcott | **97.** The Great Gatsby | **98.** The Adventures of Huckleberry Finn | **99.** Leonardo da Vinci | **100.** Fyodor Dostoevsky

WHAT'S THE
BEST TRIVIA
BOOK?

ENTERTAINMENT TRIVIA

DID YOU KNOW?

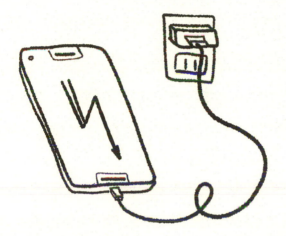

It costs less than a dollar
to charge your phone all year.

ENTERTAINMENT

HOW
DO YOU
FEEL?

1. Name the annual parade held in Pasadena, California on New Year's Day.

2. What has been the longest running show on Broadway?

3. In what videogame are Jiggies, Jinjos, and Feathers collected?

4. What famous pop singers had an iconic kiss during the 2003 MTV Video Music Awards?

5. What was the first ever videogame console?

6. The Umbrella Corporation is a fictitious company in which famous videogame?

7. What was the hometown of Fred, Wilma, Barney, and Betty?

8. C3PO and ____ are the two famous robots in Star Wars.

9. Who is the creator of the American TV show Family Guy?

10. Which party decoration was originally made from an animal's bladder?

11. What is the name of Bryan Cranston's character in the show Breaking Bad?

12. Who plays Leslie Knope in the show Parks & Recreation?

13. Who created the animated show South Park?

14. In which year was the Nintendo 64 released?

15. Supermodel Tyra Banks is known for hosting which television series?

16. Name Fred Flintstone's best friend and neighbor?

17. What does the acronym "NES" stand for?

18. Who wrote Pride and Prejudice?

19. What is the name of Ross' pet monkey in the show Friends?

20. Who played Fox Mulder in the X-Files?

Answers 1. The Rose Parade | **2.** The Phantom of the Opera | **3.** Banjo-Kazooie | **4.** Madonna and Britney Spears | **5.** Magnavox Odyssey | **6.** Resident Evil | **7.** Bedrock | **8.** R2D2 | **9.** Seth MacFarlane | **10.** Balloon | **11.** Walter White | **12.** Amy Poehler | **13.** Trey Stone and Matt Parker | **14.** 1996 | **15.** America's Next Top Model | **16.** Barney Rubble | **17.** Nintendo Entertainment System | **18.** Jane Austen | **19.** Marcel | **20.** David Duchovny

"HOW DO YOU FEEL?" ○ ○ ○

21 What is the real name of the superhero, The Flash?

22 What videogame features a soldier named Master Chief?

23 What artist designed the "Xenomorph", the famous creature in the movie Alien?

24 What was Marilyn Monroe's birth name?

25 What was Nintendo's first arcade game?

26 Where does Gonzo from the Muppet Show come from?

27 Who was the founder and leader of the X-men?

28 Name the group of heroes led by Dick Grayson.

29 Which series from the 2000s featured the characters Sheldon and Leonard?

30 Who is the villain in Super Mario Bros?

31 Where do the Munsters live?

32 In the movie Mean Girls, what color do they wear on Wednesdays?

33 What was Citizen Kane's dying word?

34 Which superhero is also known as "The Man of Steel"?

35 Name the musical play set in 1950's New York and based on Shakespeare's Romeo and Juliet.

36 To which elementary school did TV's Brady Bunch go?

37 What does the statue of Oscar stand on?

38 What is the name of the cloud-riding, glasses-wearing koopa in the Super Mario Bros. series?

39 Name the British game known as checkers in the U.S.

40 Originally, Nintendo sold which products?

Answers: 21. Barry Allen | 22. Halo | 23. H.R. Giger | 24. Norma Jeane Mortenson | 25. Donkey Kong | 26. Outer space | 27. Professor X (Charles Xavier) | 28. Titans | 29. The Big Bang Theory | 30. Bowser | 31. Mockingbird Lane | 32. Pink | 33. Rosebud | 34. Superman | 35. West Side Story | 36. Dixie Canyon Elementary | 37. A reel of film | 38. Lakitu | 39. Draughts | 40. Playing cards

NEXT OR TRY AGAIN?

ENTERTAINMENT

HOW DO YOU FEEL?

41 In Harry Potter, what do you need to say to open the Marauder's Map?

42 How many times did Ross get divorced on Friends?

43 Game of Thrones was created by whom?

44 What is Batman's real name?

45 Name Mexico's fastest mouse.

46 What day is known as Star Wars Day?

47 What is Nintendo's Mario's last name?

48 Who plays the voices of Police Chief Wiggum, Dr. Nick and Moe in 'The Simpsons'?

49 Which game takes place on the mythical island of Koholint?

50 What was the name The Mandalorian fans gave to "The Child"?

51 Name the very first video game.

52 Which pop icon shares a name with Michael Cera's character in Arrested Development?

53 Name the three animated shows written by Matt Groening.

54 What were Wilma Flintstone and Betty Rubble's surnames before they were married?

55 Who plays Dr. House?

56 Which company invented the Betamax video recorder?

57 What does "poco a poco" mean?

58 Which highly regarded TV drama was based around a dysfunctional family running a funeral parlor?

59 Which board game involves climbing and sliding.

60 In Spiderman, Uncle Ben says the famous quote: with great power comes great _____.

Answers 41. I solemnly swear that I am up to no good | **42.** Three | **43.** George R.R. Martin | **44.** Bruce Wayne | **45.** Speedy Gonzalez | **46.** May 4th | **47.** Mario | **48.** Hank Azaria | **49.** The Legend of Zelda | **50.** Baby Yoda | **51.** Pong | **52.** George Michael | **53.** The Simpsons, Futurama and Disenchantment | **54.** Slaghoople and McBricker | **55.** Hugh Laurie | **56.** Sony | **57.** Little by little | **58.** Six Feet Under | **59.** Snakes and ladders | **60.** Responsibility

61 Which animated work first featured sound?

62 Which chess term means "in passing"?

63 Name the TV show: "Brooklyn ___"

64 The rating system in Chess is called...?

65 In The Office, who bought Michael's "World's Best Boss" mug?

66 In Harry Potter, who was the Half-Blood Prince?

67 Who is the main character in Nintendo's Legend of Zelda?

68 What is Tina Turner's real name?

69 Who named his son X Æ A-12?

70 In the Marvel comics, who was Thanos's sibling?

71 What is the highest-grossing video game of all time?

72 Michelle Pfeiffer, Anne Hathaway, Halle Berry and Zoe Kravitz have all played which character?

73 Mario first appeared as a character in which videogame?

74 Which U.S. TV show is the longest running live-action show?

75 Captain America's shield is made out of what?

76 What was the original name of The Little Rascals?

77 What fictional character is found naked and wrapped in plastic in Twin Peaks?

78 Who is James Bond's often returning nemesis?

79 Who invented the hovercraft?

80 What turn of phrase did Clark Kent's boss often use?

Answers 61. Disney's Steamboat Willie | 62. En passant | 63. Nine-Nine | 64. Elo | 65. Himself | 66. Severus Snape | 67. Link | 68. Anna Mae Bullock | 69. Elon Musk | 70. Fox (Starfox) | 71. Minecraft | 72. Catwoman | 73. Donkey Kong | 74. Law & Order | 75. Vibranium | 76. Our Gang | 77. Laura Palmer | 78. Ernst Stavro Blofeld | 79. Sir Christopher Cockerell | 80. Great Caesar's Ghost!

NEXT OR TRY AGAIN?

81 What was Charles Schultz originally going to call Peanuts?

82 What is the name of Bart Simpson's teacher?

83 In "Breaking Bad" which actor played Walter White?

84 Which manned aircraft first exceeded the speed of sound?

85 What instrument does Ted Mosby steal in How I Met Your Mother?

86 In Bewitched, what part of her body does Samantha move in order to make magic?

87 Name the first game cartridge to include a battery backed save feature?

88 What kind of animal is a "koopa"?

89 Which X-Men villain is also a Holocaust survivor?

90 What is the X-Files famous poster phrase?

91 What kind of car is Barbie's pink sports car?

92 Name the final and hardest track in Mario Kart videogames.

93 Wolverine's skeleton is bonded to which substance?

94 Which cube puzzle was created by a Hungarian mathematician in the 1970s?

95 What modern-day object was accidentally filmed in Game Of Thrones' final season?

96 Name the late-night American TV show famous for its sketch comedy and special musical guests.

97 In the Marvel universe, how many Infinity Stones are there?

98 What sci-fi horror Netflix show is set in Hawkins, Indiana?

99 Which superhero gets his power from a ring?

100 Which TV show's title comes from a real medical textbook and has been running for 18 seasons?

Answers 81. Li'l Folks | 82. Edna Krabappel | 83. Bryan Cranston | 84. Bell X-1 | 85. A blue French horn | 86. Her nose | 87. The Legend of Zelda | 88. A turtle | 89. Magneto | 90. I Want To Believe | 91. Corvette | 92. Rainbow Road | 93. Adamantium | 94. Rubik | 95. A Starbucks cup | 96. SNL | 97. Seven | 98. Stranger Things | 99. Green Lantern | 100. Grey's Anatomy

WHAT'S THE
BEST TRIVIA
BOOK?

MOVIES TRIVIA

DID YOU KNOW?

1 OUT OF EVERY 4 AMERICANS HAS APPEARED ON TV IN THEIR LIFETIME.

MOVIES

1. Which scary movie character has the real name of Charles Lee Ray?

2. What popular Disney film tells the story of an ice queen and her sister?

3. Which actresses won an Oscar by playing respectively, Margaret Thatcher and Queen Elizabeth II?

4. In the Harry Potter film franchise, what does the Hogwarts motto "Draco dormiens nunquam titillandus" mean?

5. What is the name of the famous Volkswagen in the film, The Love Bug?

6. Name the famous 1950's American actor who filmed 3 movies and tragically died aged 24.

7. Who framed Roger Rabbit?

8. In "Forrest Gump" who loved shrimp?

9. John McClane was the hero in which eighties movie?

10. Allison Janney won the Oscar for Best Supporting Actress in 2017 for her role as the mom of which famous American ice skater?

11. Which plant was Uma Thurman's character in Batman & Robin named for?

12. Wakanda is the fictitious country setting for which movie?

13. On whom did Dorothy's house land in The Wizard Of Oz?

14. A love scene in Honey, I Shrunk The Kids occurs inside what?

15. Which horror movie killer's look is based on the painting "The Scream" by Edvard Munch?

16. "Snakes, I hate snakes" is a line from which film?

17. Who composed the music for Jurassic Park?

18. Which film starring Robert Downey Jr. depicts superheroes teaming up to fight the villain, Thanos?

19. What 1981 film with an athletic theme won the Oscar for Best Film in 1982?

20. How many storm troopers were there on screen in Star Trek?

Answers 1. Chucky | **2.** Frozen | **3.** Meryl Streep and Helen Mirren | **4.** Never tickle a sleeping dragon | **5.** Herbie | **6.** James Dean | **7.** Judge Doom | **8.** Bubba | **9.** Die Hard | **10.** Tonya Harding | **11.** Poison Ivy | **12.** Black Panther | **13.** The Wicked Witch of the East | **14.** A lego brick | **15.** Ghost Face from Scream | **16.** Indiana Jones: Raiders of The Lost Ark | **17.** John Williams | **18.** Avengers: Endgame | **19.** Chariots of Fire | **20.** None (it was Star Wars)

HOW DO YOU FEEL?

21 In The Matrix, which color pill is taken by Neo?

22 Dory, from the movie Finding Nemo is voiced by ___.

23 Who directed the first Halloween movie?

24 The Lord of The Rings movies were filmed in which country?

25 Name the movie adaptation of the famous sci-fi novel by Frank Herbert.

26 Jurassic Park III was directed by whom?

27 Who was the first black actress to win an Oscar?

28 Which planet does Anakin Skywalker come from?

29 Which actor won an Oscar for her part in Nomadland?

30 Who sang "New York New York" in the film of the same name?

31 What Rizzo's real name in the movie, Grease?

32 Who plays himself in the movie Zombieland?

33 Which film about the March sisters starred Florence Pugh and Saoirse Ronan?

34 In the movie Halloween, what was Michael Myers middle name?

35 What country does Forrest Gump travel to as part of the American ping-pong team?

36 Name the film starring Rosie O'Donnell, Rita Wilson and Meg Ryan?

37 What was Han Solo's ship in Star Wars called?

38 In which fictional world is The Lord of The Rings set ?

39 Which movie was incorrectly announced as Best Picture winner in the 2017 Academy Awards?

40 What is the term for the iconic cowboy movies produced and filmed in Europe, mainly in Italy?

Answers21. Red | **22.** Ellen DeGeneres | **23.** John Carpenter | **24.** New Zealand | **25.** Dune | **26.** Joe Johnston | **27.** Hattie McDaniel | **28.** Tatooine | **29.** Frances McDormand | **30.** Liza Minelli | **31.** Betty | **32.** Bill Murray | **33.** Little Women | **34.** Audrey | **35.** China | **36.** Sleepless in Seattle | **37.** Millennium Falcon | **38.** Middle Earth | **39.** La La Land | **40.** Spaghetti Westerns

NEXT OR TRY AGAIN?

MOVIES

HOW
DO YOU
FEEL?

41 Finish this tag line from the trailer for the film Alien. "In space no one can____."

42 Name the famous archaeologist portrayed by Harrison Ford.

43 The movie Clueless starring Alicia Silverstone is actually an adaptation of which Jane Austen novel?

44 Four Weddings and a Funeral later had "an equal, not a sequel". What was it called?

45 Who played Batman in Tim Burton's 1989 film?

46 Which kind of creature is Mr. Tumnus in Narnia?

47 Starring Meryl Streep and Anne Hathaway, which 2006 film was about a powerful fashion magazine editor and her assistant?

48 Who directed the 2017 horror movie Get Out?

49 In which horror movie did Johnny Depp make his film debut?

50 What was Steven Spielberg's 1975 first hit?

51 Harry Potter owns what kind of animal?

52 Who did Alec Guinness play in Star Wars?

53 Which actress has been nominated for the most Academy Awards?

54 Which 1988 film saw Bruce Willis battling against a group of terrorists that rudely interrupted a Christmas party?

55 Name the only foreign film to win Best Picture at the Academy Awards.

56 What was Melissa Matheson's contribution to E.T.?

57 Which Marvel movie comes first in chronological order?

58 Who played The Joker in Christopher Nolan's The Dark Knight?

59 What movie holds the record for the worldwide highest-grossing film?

60 James Dean died during the filming of which movie in 1955?

Answers 41. *Hear you scream* | 42. *Indiana Jones* | 43. *Emma* | 44. *Notting Hill* | 45. *Michael Keaton* | 46. *He is a faun* | 47. *The Devil Wears Prada* | 48. *Jordan Peele* | 49. *A Nightmare on Elm Street* | 50. *Close Encounters of the Third Kind* | 51. *His snowy owl, Hedwig* | 52. *Obi-Wan Kenobi* | 53. *Meryl Streep* | 54. *Die Hard* | 55. *Parasite* | 56. *Scriptwriter* | 57. *Captain America: The First Avenger* | 58. *Heath Ledger* | 59. *Avatar (2009)* | 60. *Giant*.

MOVIES

HOW
DO YOU
FEEL?

WHAT'S THE
BEST TRIVIA
BOOK?

49

61 What unique gift did Harry Potter get for Christmas in his first semester at Hogwarts School?

62 What was Audrey Hepburn's birth name?

63 Tall Dark And Gruesome is the autobiography of which star?

64 Dunkirk, the movie depicting the evacuation of WWII soldiers was directed by whom?

65 In the movie Godzilla, what is the Japanese name for Godzilla?

66 Which James Bond movie takes place over Christmas?

67 Who directed all of The Lord of The Rings movies?

68 How many films are there in the Jaws series?

69 In the 1996 film of Romeo and Juliet, who was Juliet played by?

70 In the movie Casablanca, which actor played the part of Rick Blaine?

71 For the Indiana Jones character, where did George Lucas get the name "Indiana"?

72 What kind of car did Doc and Marty drive?

73 The thinnest film is made from which metal?

74 In Star Wars, who are Kylo Ren's parents?

75 In The Lord of The Rings, what was Gollum's hobbit name?

76 Which Harry Potter actor also starred in Dracula?

77 Which Star Wars movie cameos aliens from Steven Spielberg's 1982 film E.T. the Extra-Terrestrial?

78 Where was the movie Call Me By Your Name filmed?

79 Which actor played "Robin" to Val Kilmer's "Batman"?

80 Who starred in the movie "The Mask"?

Answers 61. *An invisibility cloak* | 62. *Audrey Kathleen Ruston* | 63. *Christopher Lee* | 64. *Christopher Nolan* | 65. *Gojira* | 66. *On Her Majesty's Secret Service* | 67. *Peter Jackson* | 68. *4 (Jaws 1, 2, 3 & Jaws The Revenge)* | 69. *Claire Danes* | 70. *Humphrey Bogart* | 71. *From his dog* | 72. *Delorean* | 73. *Gold* | 74. *Han Solo and Princess Leia* | 75. *Smeagol* | 76. *Gary Oldman* | 77. *Star Wars Episode I: The Phantom Menace* | 78. *Italy* | 79. *Christopher O'Donnell* | 80. *Jim Carrey*

NEXT
OR TRY AGAIN?

MOVIES

HOW DO YOU FEEL?

START

81 What 1992 horror movie remade in 2021 was directed by Jordan Peele?

82 Robert Mitchum acted in the 60s original, and Robert de Niro in the remake in 1991. What was the title of both movies?

83 In Star Wars who killed Qui-Gon Jinn?

84 In the 1999 version of The Mummy, what is the mummy called?

85 In Herbie Fully Loaded, who plays Maggie Payton's father?

86 What is the name of the famous pirate played by Johnny Depp in the movie Pirates of The Caribbean?

87 For which movie did Leonardo DiCaprio win his first and only Oscar?

88 What was Anne Hathaway's big screen debut movie?

89 Who originally played Obi-Wan Kenobi in Star Wars?

90 Who plays Legolas in The Lord of The Rings?

91 Who played the part of the Tokyo underworld boss O-Ren Ishii in Kill Bill I and II?

92 Which Mexican film director won the Best Director and Best Film Oscars for his film "The Shape of Water"?

93 Name the second movie Olivia Newton John and John Travolta starred in together?

94 A succession of 48 baby pigs were used in the title role for which 1995 hit movie?

95 James Dean starred in three films. What were they?

96 What were the three main rules in Gremlins?

97 What is the highest-grossing Marvel film?

98 Who was the first woman to win the "Best Director" category at the Oscars?

99 Who played the medium Oda Mae Brown in Ghost?

100 FINISH What was the first Disney animated film to earn Best Picture nomination in the Academy Awards?

Answers 81. *Candyman* | 82. *Cape Fear* | 83. *Darth Maul* | 84. *Imhotep* | 85. *Michael Keaton* | 86. *Jack Sparrow* | 87. *The Revenant* | 88. *The Princess Diaries* | 89. *Alec Guinness* | 90. *Orlando Bloom* | 91. *Lucy Liu* | 92. *Guillermo del Toro* | 93. *Two of a Kind* | 94. *Babe* | 95. *A Rebel Without a Cause, East of Eden, Giant* | 96. *Don't expose it to light, don't let it get wet and never feed it after midnight.* | 97. *Avengers: Endgame* | 98. *Kathryn Bigelow (for The Hurt Locker in 2010)* | 99. *Whoopi Goldberg* | 100. *Beauty and the Beast*

WHAT'S THE
BEST TRIVIA
BOOK?

MUSIC TRIVIA

DID YOU KNOW?

SWEARING CAN ACTUALLY HELP
TO RELIEVE PHYSICAL PAIN.

MUSIC

1. What style of dancing was popularized with rap music?

2. Music record discs are made of which material?

3. Complete the lyrics. "I am the eggman, they are the Eggmen, I am ___ _____ " (2 Words).

4. Aretha Franklin was the first woman inducted into what?

5. What is the name of the lead singer in the popular band Led Zeppelin?

6. What is the name of Coldplay's debut album?

7. Name Britney Spears' first single.

8. What is the name of the object used by musicians to place and read their paper scores or sheets of music?

9. Who was the first American Idol winner?

10. Phil Collins was the lead singer of which band?

11. Heartbreak Hotel is a song by which iconic singer.

12. Who is the lead singer of The Smiths?

13. The Beatles' "All You Need Is Love" began with what piece of music?

14. Who wrote the operas The Magic Flute and The Marriage of Figaro?

15. The movie Back to the Future featured a song entitled "Back in Time" by which band?

16. What was the title of Ike and Tina Turner's only album?

17. Who was the Beatles' original drummer?

18. Which guitarist used a sixpence to play his instrument?

19. What is Johnny Rotten's real name?

20. What is the term for a symphonical musical piece formed with fragments of other works?

Answers 1. Hip-hop | **2.** Vinyl | **3.** The Walrus | **4.** The Rock & Roll Hall Of Fame | **5.** Robert Plant | **6.** Parachutes | **7.** Baby One More Time | **8.** Music stand | **9.** Kelly Clarkson | **10.** Genesis | **11.** Elvis Presley | **12.** Morrissey | **13.** The French National Anthem/»La Marseillaise« | **14.** Mozart | **15.** Huey Lewis and The News | **16.** River Deep, Mountain High | **17.** Pete Best | **18.** Brian May | **19.** John Lydon | **20.** Rhapsody

21 Ozzy Osbourne was the lead vocalist of which heavy metal band?

22 In which U.S. State is the Rock and Roll Hall of Fame?

23 Who wrote the famous song "Jolene"?

24 In the 60s, who was "Shakin' All Over"?

25 "Also Sprach Zarathustra" was the music for which Stanley Kubrick film?

26 What is the name of the Pink Floyd album featuring a prism on its cover?

27 Who is the signer known as the "First Lady of Country Music"?

28 The musical version of the play Pygmalion is known as?

29 What inflatable featured in Pink Floyd's 1977 tour?

30 Name the last single released by John Lennon.

31 Who is known as the father of country music?

32 Who was John Lennon's father?

33 Which singer's real name is Robyn Fenty?

34 Which U.S. clarinetist's real name was Arthur Jacob Shaw?

35 The word xylophone comes from the Greek words for what?

36 Who released Blood On The Tracks?

37 Who "Let The Dogs Out"?

38 Which ex-member of the Latin teen group Menudo enjoyed worldwide success?

39 In musical notation, what is the name of the symbol placed at the beginning of the staff?

40 Which classical music composer, one of the greatest of all time, died blind?

Answers 21. Black Sabbath | 22. Ohio | 23. Dolly Parton | 24. Johnny Kidd And The Pirates | 25. 2001: A Space Odyssey | 26. Dark Side of The Moon | 27. Tammy Wynette | 28. My Fair Lady | 29. A Pig | 30. (Just Like) Starting Over | 31. Jimmie Rodgers | 32. Alfred «Freddie» Lennon | 33. Rihanna | 34. Artie Shaw | 35. Wood & Sound | 36. Bob Dylan | 37. Baha Men | 38. Ricky Martin | 39. Clef or Key | 40. Johann Sebastian Bach

MUSIC

41 Who is known as "The King of Country"?

42 Ice Ice Baby is a song by which band?

43 How many members does the famous Korean band BTS have?

44 What is the smallest grand piano?

45 Lesane Parish Crooks is an American rapper known as what?

46 Name the subgenre of country music, developed in the Appalachian region and traditionally played on acoustic stringed instruments.

47 Who recorded the hit "Tonight, Tonight"?

48 The Beatles covered the song "Chains". Who was the original artist?

49 In 1988, this jazz player fell to his death from a window in Amsterdam. Who was it?

50 An orchestra consists of how many groups of instruments?

51 During their 1964 world tour, who filled in for the Beatles' Ringo Starr?

52 Singer Stefani Joanne Angelina Germanotta is best known as who?

53 Which famous song by Luis Fonzi and Daddy Yankee topped the chart in 47 countries in 2017?

54 Which rock star once tried to bite the head off a bat during a gig?

55 Name the section of the orchestra that usually has the most musicians.

56 Where was Justin Bieber first discovered?

57 Who is best-selling female artist of all time?

58 Who is considered The King of Pop?

59 Name the first George Harrison composition recorded by the Beatles.

60 Born Roberta Streeter, which artist wrote their first single about a man's suicide in "Ode To Billy Joe"?

Answers 41. George Harvey Strait Sr. | **42.** Vanilla Ice | **43.** Seven | **44.** Petit grand | **45.** Tupac | **46.** Bluegrass | **47.** Hot Chelle Rae | **48.** The Cookies | **49.** Chet Baker | **50.** Four | **51.** Jimmy Nicol | **52.** Lady Gaga | **53.** Despacito | **54.** Ozzy Osbourne | **55.** String | **56.** YouTube | **57.** Madonna | **58.** Michael Jackson | **59.** Don't Bother Me | **60.** Robbie Gentry

61 Who became, in 2020 the youngest person to ever win a Grammy for album of the year?

62 What is the term for music performed by a singer or a singing group without any instrumental accompaniment?

63 Which instruments are also known as the kettledrum?

64 What genre of music originated in South Korea and has taken the world by storm?

65 Who is "The Queen of Soul"?

66 Bach, Handel and Vivaldi are associated which music era?

67 For what reason did The Jackson 5 change their name to The Jacksons?

68 In which U.S. city did "Grunge" music originate?

69 What function did Franz Schubert perform at Beethoven's funeral?

70 Which Beach Boy joined the Beatles on their visit to the Maharishi?

71 What is the most ancient wind instrument in the world?

72 ABBA comes from which European country?

73 What is Justin Bieber's fanbase name?

74 What was originally called "hillbilly music" during the 1950s?

75 What is Paul McCartney's estimated worth?

76 Royals was nominated for Song of the Year at the 2014 Grammy Awards, sang by whom?

77 Where did the first U.S. live Beatles concert take place?

78 Who is known as "The Queen of Disco"?

79 Bjork was originally a member of which band?

80 What was Stevie Wonder's first album after getting control of his work in 1972?

Answers 61. Billy Eilish | 62. A capella | 63. Tympani | 64. K-Pop | 65. Aretha Franklin | 66. Baroque Period | 67. Motown owned the name The Jackson 5, and they were moving to Epic Records. | 68. Seattle | 69. He was a pallbearer | 70. Mike Love | 71. Flute | 72. Sweden | 73. Beliebers | 74. Country music | 75. 1.2 billion | 76. Lorde | 77. Washington D.C. | 78. Donna Summer | 79. The Sugarcubes | 80. Music On My Mind

NEXT OR TRY AGAIN?

MUSIC

81 Name the singer, actor, producer and former member of the band NSYNC.

82 Which instrument gives the tuning note to the rest of the orchestra?

83 Which Guns N' Roses video did Arnold Schwarzenegger appear in?

84 What instrument is smaller, a violin, a cello, or a contrabass?

85 Jon Buckland, Guy Berryman, Chris Martin and Will Champion are members of which famous band?

86 Shawn Mendes and which Cuban-American singer perform the famous song "Señorita" together?

87 Who won the first official Gold Record?

88 Name the popular music of Jamaican origins.

89 What famous U.S. festival hosted around 350 thousand people in 1969?

90 Name the stringed instrument in the guitar family with the round shape of a tambourine, used in folk music and bluegrass.

91 Where is karaoke originally from?

92 Paul McCartney recorded duets with which two Motown artists?

93 What is the world's best-selling album of all time?

94 Name the dance popularized by Michael Jackson in 1983.

95 Name the electronic music duo famous for using robot suits.

96 Richard Wagner composed organ music or operas?

97 Frank Sinatra had 2 No.1s in the 60s. What were they?

98 Name the four groups of musical instruments in an orchestra.

99 Finish the name of this Christina Aguilera track "Genie In A ..."?

100 Influenced by punk rock, which genre was first used to describe guitar bands like Nirvana and Pearl Jam during the 1990s?

Answers 81. Justin Timberlake | 82. Oboe | 83. You could be Mine | 84. Violin | 85. Coldplay | 86. Camila Cabello | 87. Perry Como in 1958 | 88. Reggae | 89. Woodstock | 90. Banjo | 91. Japan | 92. Stevie Wonder & Michael Jackson | 93. Michael Jackson's Thriller | 94. The Moonwalk | 95. Daft Punk | 96. Operas | 97. Strangers in The Night / Something Stupid | 98. Wind, string, brass and percussion | 99. Bottle | 100. Grunge

WHAT'S THE
BEST TRIVIA
BOOK?

SPORTS & LEISURE
TRIVIA

DID YOU KNOW?

TOP EXPORT FROM THE USA IS CARS.
TOP IMPORT TO THE USA IS ALSO CARS.

SPORTS & LEISURE

1. An archery target features which five colors?

2. Name the only Major League team to ever win a best-of-seven series after losing the first three games.

3. How many teams qualify for the FIFA World Cup?

4. Who is known as "The Greatest Heavyweight Boxer of All Time"?

5. Which sport uses the most body equipment?

6. In the Olympic Games, what are the four standard throwing events?

7. How many players does a volleyball team have?

8. In golf, when does a player make a "birdie"?

9. What was the highest ever scoring NFL game?

10. What sport area did president Barack Obama install in the White House?

11. What are the names of the three different weapons used in fencing?

12. What Major League player was the first to pitch a ball over 100 mph?

13. Bjorn Borg won how many consecutive Wimbledon titles?

14. In a game of polo, what is the period of play called?

15. Which Chicago Bears running back was known as "The Galloping Ghost"?

16. What Major League pitcher has the record for the most Cy Young Awards?

17. Who beat Mike Tyson in 1990 to become the World Heavyweight Boxing Champion?

18. Who won for the eighth time, the Australian Open in 2020?

19. What's the only NFL team that has gone undefeated and won the Super Bowl?

20. In which way does the bishop moves in a game of chess?

Answers 1. Gold, Red, Blue, Black, White | 2. Boston Red Sox (2004) | 3. 32 (The 2026 FIFA World Cup will feature 16 more teams) | 4. Muhammad Ali | 5. Ice hockey | 6. Shot put, discus, hammer and javelin | 7. 6 Players | 8. When he uses one stroke less than the par of the hole. | 9. Washington Redskins (Commanders) in 1966 with 72 points | 10. Basketball court | 11. Epee, Foil and Sabre | 12. Nolan Ryan in 1974 | 13. 5 | 14. Chukka or Chukker | 15. Harold "Red" Grange | 16. Roger Clemens "The Rocket" | 17. James Buster Douglas | 18. Novak Djokovic | 19. Miami Dolphins (1972) | 20. Diagonally

21 Which country held the 1992 Olympics?

22 Who first won the U.S. Masters five times?

23 In which Grand Slam tournament is white dress required?

24 Which is the only country to have played in every FIFA World Cup?

25 Which tennis player has won 12 Roland Garros titles?

26 Who played the match known as the "Game of the Century" in the 1970 FIFA World Cup?

27 Which NFL team has appeared most often in the Super Bowl?

28 In which year did the first modern Olympic Games take place?

29 What is the "perfect score" in a game of Ten Pin Bowling?

30 Who was the youngest Formula One driver to win a race?

31 Name three tennis players born in Germany between 1950 And 2000 that have won the Wimbledon Men's Singles title?

32 How many World Series have the Chicago Cubs won?

33 Where did the game of polo originate?

34 Which is heavier? An ice hockey puck or a baseball?

35 Who preceded Tiger Woods as the number one ranked golfer in 1998?

36 "Behind & Banana Kick" are terms in which sport?

37 Which country won the 2019 FIFA Women's World Cup?

38 What is the rarest hand in poker?

39 What are the names of the two conferences that make up the NFL?

40 How many bases does a baseball field have?

Answers 21. Barcelona, Spain | **22.** Jack Nicklaus | **23.** Wimbledon | **24.** Brazil | **25.** Rafael Nadal | **26.** Italy-Germany | **27.** The New England Patriots (11 times) | **28.** In 1896 | **29.** 300 | **30.** Max Verstappen (when he was 17 years old) | **31.** Boris Becker, John McEnroe & Michael Stich | **32.** Three | **33.** Persia (Iran) | **34.** An Ice Hockey puck | **35.** Greg Norman | **36.** Australian Football League | **37.** United States | **38.** A Royal Flush | **39.** American Football Conference and National Football Conference | **40.** Four

SPORTS & LEISURE

41 Name the four regulation strokes in swimming.

42 Which country defeated France, winning the 2018 FIFA World Cup?

43 Megan Rapinoe, the professional soccer player is also known by which nickname?

44 What is the national sport of Canada?

45 What is the letter K worth in Scrabble?

46 Name the squash shot where the ball hits the side of the wall first.

47 You would "Catch a Crab" in which sport?

48 What's the main feature of a speedway motorbike?

49 Which three winter sports were introduced as official events at the 1998 Winter Olympic games?

50 Which 2 players scored for the U.S. in the 2019 Women's World Cup?

51 Which American football team won the 2006 Super Bowl?

52 Where does the Kentucky derby take place?

53 The winner of a Formula One Grand Prix is awarded how many points?

54 What is the name for the white outfits used in Karate and Judo?

55 In which sport is Lewis Hamilton a leading competitor?

56 Which swimming stroke is not started by a dive?

57 What is the name of the object a runner transfers in a relay race?

58 The first televised Olympic Games were the Tokyo Olympics in what year?

59 "Outcrop," "Big Wall" and "Crag" are all types of what?

60 Who was first person to climb "Silence", the highest climbing route in the world?

Answers 41. Backstroke, Butterfly, Breaststroke and Freestyle | **42.** Croatia | **43.** Pinoe | **44.** Lacrosse | **45.** 5 Points | **46.** A Boast | **47.** Rowing | **48.** No brake | **49.** Snowboarding, curling and women's ice hocke | **50.** Megan Rapinoe and Rose Lavell | **51.** New England Patriots | **52.** Louisville, Kentuck | **53.** Ten Points | **54.** Gi | **55.** Formula One | **56.** Backstroke | **57.** Baton | **58.** 1964 | **59.** Rock Climbing | **60.** Adam Ondra

LOUIS RICHARDS

61 Having won 11 world titles, who is considered to be the best surfer?

62 Which famous NBA player has also played in the MLB?

63 Who was the first player to be drafted in the NFL?

64 Which climber is known for his solo climbing of El Capitan in Yosemite National Park?

65 How many players are there in an ice hockey team?

66 Football is derived from which English sport?

67 Name the first NHL player to score 50 goals in one season.

68 Which famous U.S. race ended in 2013 with a terrorist attack?

69 In backgammon, how many pieces per player are there?

70 Name the four tournaments that make up the Grand Slam.

71 What testing was first carried out at the 1968 Olympics?

72 Which city was the host of the first modern Olympic Games?

73 Who would use a penholder grip?

74 Name soccer's international governing board.

75 Which tennis player has won more Grand Slam singles titles than any other?

76 Which team won the LIV Super Bowl, after waiting for 50 years?

77 Gianmarco Tamberi and Mutaz Barshim shared a gold medal in which sport at the 2020 Olympics?

78 In chess, how many pieces per player are there?

79 The AT&T Stadium is home to which football team?

80 Which sporting event takes place every year on Memorial Day weekend?

Answers 61. Kelly Slater | 62. Michael Jordan | 63. Jay Berwanger in 1936 | 64. Alex Honnold | 65. 6 | 66. Rugby | 67. Maurice Richard | 68. Boston Marathon | 69. 15 Pieces | 70. Wimbledon, Rolland Garros, U.S. Open, Australian Open | 71. Drug Testing | 72. Athens (1896) | 73. A Table Tennis Player | 74. FIFA | 75. Serena Williams | 76. Kansas City Chiefs | 77. High Jump | 78. 16 Pieces | 79. Dallas Cowboys | 80. Indianapolis 500

NEXT? OR TRY AGAIN?

SPORTS & LEISURE

WHAT'S THE
**BEST TRIVIA
BOOK?**

60

HOW :-(○
DO YOU :-| ○
FEEL? :-) ○

81 What football player rushed for 2,003 yards in 1973?

82 What martial art debuted at the 2000 Olympic Games?

83 What chess move allows you to move two pieces at the same time?

84 How many people are on a Tug-of-War team?

85 Name the 3 balls used in a game of Billiards.

86 Which class is the lowest weight in professional boxing?

87 Which team won the LIII Super Bowl, matching the six-game win record?

88 What does the ringing of a bell mean in athletic track races?

89 Which sportswear company uses three stripes to signify their brand?

90 Which race is celebrated in memory of the Greek soldier Pheidippides?

91 How many consecutive outs does a pitcher need in order to have a perfect game?

92 What legendary baseball player was also known as "The Bambino"?

93 What is referred to by a "Mashie"?

94 What were the 5 sports added to the Olympic Games in 2020?

95 Which professional skater is known for having landed the world's first 900?

96 Which sports make up a Triathlon?

97 What was the first sport played on the Moon?

98 How many NBA championships did Koby Bryant win with the LA Lakers?

99 Who is considered to be the fastest man on earth?

100 What are the 4 ways of scoring in professional football?

Answers 81. OJ Simpson | 82. Tae Kwon Do | 83. Castling | 84. 8 People | 85. White, Spot, Red | 86. Straw Weight | 87. New England Patriots | 88. The Last Lap | 89. Adidas | 90. Marathon | 91. 27 | 92. Babe Ruth | 93. A type of golf club | 94. Baseball/softball, karate, sport climbing, surfing and skateboarding | 95. Tony Hawk | 96. Swimming, Cycling and Running | 97. Golf | 98. 5 | 99. Usain Bolt | 100. Touchdown, Field Goal, Safety, Try

WHAT'S THE
BEST TRIVIA
BOOK?

FUN
FACTS

FUN FACTS

1	There are no words that rhyme with orange.
2	Solar energy is heat from the sun that is captured and used, and it is an environment-friendly source of energy.
3	The U.S. is the biggest coffee user in the world.
4	The first trains' top speed was only 8 km/h (5 mph).
5	11% of all people write with their left hands.
6	There are 13 letters in the Hawaiian alphabet.
7	Pizza was born in Naples and the signature dish was named after Queen Margherita.
8	Abraham Lincoln lost five different elections prior to becoming a U.S. president.

9	Due to contrasts in gravity, a person normally weighing 200 pounds will weigh just 76 pounds on Mars.
10	The postal service in the United States was free of charge until 1863.
11	The most widely used word in English speech is 'I'.
12	There are more chickens than there are humans.
13	Diamonds are the natural substance that is the hardest.
14	There's a tree named the Idiot Fruit that grows in the Daintree rainforest of Australia.
15	The only word that begins and ends with the letters 'und' is the word' underground.'
16	The letter most frequently used in the alphabet is E.
17	The fear of trees is called dendrophobia.

PIGS ARE UNABLE TO LOOK UP AT THE SKY.

FUN FACTS

18	Recycling a glass jar will save enough energy for 3 hours of TV.
19	The use of search engines such as Google and Bing are one of the best and most regular ways to find information on the web. Google is currently the most popular search engine and receives hundreds of millions of search queries daily.
20	The United States first introduced credit cards in the 1920's.
21	Four is the only number with the same number of letters.
22	While bacteria can be treated with antibiotics, it is not effective against a virus.
23	Leonardo da Vinci outlined designs for a humanoid robot in 1495. A lot of robot prototypes are being made today.
24	The number 2 is the only number larger than zero that gives you the same result when added or multiplied by itself (4).
25	For his theoretical physics research, Albert Einstein was awarded the Nobel Prize in Physics in 1921.

THERE ARE VERY HIGH LEVELS OF ANTIOXIDANTS IN BLUEBERRIES.

26 Many bygone presidents are shown on US dollar bills, such as George Washington ($1), Abraham Lincoln ($5), Andrew Jackson ($20), and Benjamin Franklin ($100).

27 You can hold more cold water with a sponge than hot water.

28 History's shortest war carried on for just 38 minutes.

29 A tsunami can move at the same speed as a jet plane.

30 Money's buying power is, over time, lessened by inflation.

31 Physical coins were first minted about 2500 years ago.

32 Around 1970, plastic bottles were first implemented for soft drinks.

33 The common cold can be caused by more than 100 various types of viruses.

34 In Sesame Street, the characters Bert and Ernie were modeled after Bert the policeman and Ernie the taxi driver from Frank Capra's It's a Wonderful Life.

THE NUMBER ONE FOOD CRAVED BY WOMEN IS CHOCOLATE.

FUN FACTS

35 The first televisions were sold in the late 1920s.

36 Tropical storms and hurricanes were officially given names from 1953.

37 The government owns 32 percent of all U.S. property.

38 A gigayear is 1,000,000,000,000 years.

39 You could fit almost 900 trillion footballs into the Grand Canyon.

40 The first keys and ignitions for cars were implemented in 1949.

41 In 1911, the first U.S. coast-to-coast airplane flight lasted 49 days.

42 Rio de Janeiro means River of January.

43 The smallest robot, a helicopter measuring 7cm high and weighing 10 grams, is released by Epsom. It is intended to be a flying camera during natural disasters.

ROASTING COFFEE BEANS BURNS OFF CAFFEINE, SO DARK ROASTED COFFEE BEANS CONTAIN LESS CAFFEINE THAN MEDIUM ROASTED ONES.

FUN FACTS

44 There is carbon in every living thing on Earth.

45 It takes more than 50,000 years for a plastic container to begin decomposing.

46 Disney Studios released the first full-length animated film in 1937, which was Snow White and the seven dwarfs.

47 The burning of fossil fuels consumes more than 86% of the energy used in the United States.

48 As a technique of identification, the Chinese used fingerprints as far back as AD 700.

49 Writing in red ink in Portugal is thought to be rude.

50 Some tumors may produce hair, teeth, bones, and even fingernails.

51 Sometimes when you're sleeping, your brain is busier than when you're awake.

52 It is prohibited to hug a tree in China.

THE SUN IS AS BIG AS ONE MILLION EARTHS.

FUN FACTS

53 Scotland has the highest number of redheads.

54 All Earth's inhabitants could fit into a cube of 1 km.

55 Annually, 13 people die from vending machines.

56 There are 336 dimples in the typical golf ball.

57 In the Amazon, giant water lilies can grow more than 6 feet in diameter.

58 Do not eat too many carrots as it may turn your skin orange.

59 In Japan, you can buy eel flavored ice cream.

60 The time shown on a watch in many adverts is 10:10.

61 Eighty percent of all people that are hit by lightning are men.

IT RAINS METAL ON THE PLANET VENUS.

62 Coca-Cola had cocaine as an ingredient in the beginning.

63 If your DNA was spread out it could reach the moon 6000 times.

64 There are specks of gold in your hair.

65 The left and right sides of your body are controlled by the opposite sides of your brain.

66 Normal soda cans will sink in water, while diet soda cans will float.

67 In Japan you can buy square watermelons, created to stack more easily in supermarkets.

68 More money is printed for Monopoly sets each day, than for the U.S. Treasury.

69 Calcium in our bones and iron in our blood are products of very old giant star explosions.

70 Initially, the yo-yo was used as a tool for hunting in the Philippines.

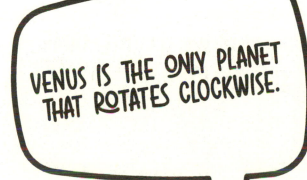

VENUS IS THE ONLY PLANET THAT ROTATES CLOCKWISE.

71 Whale poo is an ingredient in some perfumes.

72 There is a pill that can make your poo smell like chocolate.

73 In their life, the typical person spends two weeks waiting for traffic lights.

74 When it freezes, water swells by 9%. Ice weighs less than water, which is why it floats.

75 Petrol has no common freezing point (it can freeze anywhere from -82 to -115C (-180 and -240F).

76 Clouds appear white as they reflect sunlight from above.

77 The speed of sound travels at approximately 1,230 km/h (767 mph).

78 Born in 1882, Emmy Noether was identified by Einstein as the most influential woman in mathematics history. She was a German mathematician who contributed significantly to abstract algebra and theoretical physics.

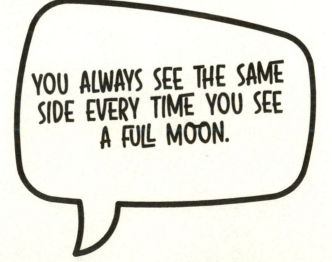

YOU ALWAYS SEE THE SAME SIDE EVERY TIME YOU SEE A FULL MOON.

79 Asimov's Three Laws of Robotics are: 1. A robot may not injure a human being or, through inaction, allow a human being to come to harm. 2. A robot must obey any orders given to it by human beings, except where such orders would conflict with the First Law. 3. A robot must protect its own existence as long as such protection does not conflict with the First or Second Law.

80 Lightning can strike twice.

81 Humidity (not air) causes drying of super glue.

82 Light journeys from the sun to Earth in 8 minutes and 19 seconds.

83 Wild lions usually do not kill more than 20 times a year.

84 Some dinosaurs aged to be over 100 years old.

85 Elephants are the only creatures to mourn the dead, apart from humans.

THE BRIGHTEST MAN-MADE LOCATION SEEN FROM SPACE IS LAS VEGAS.

FUN FACTS

86 Elephants can sing by using an ultrasound rumble so low that humans cannot hear it. They use it to keep the herd together, and to find mates.

87 In under a minute, Komodo dragons will eat five pounds of meat. They reserve any additional fat they eat in their tails.

88 Crocodiles by the banks of the Nile river are accountable for over 1000 deaths per annum.

89 An elephant never forgets.

90 The African Rock Python will live without food for two years.

91 It takes less than 3 minutes for a camel to consume 94 liters (25 gallons) of water.

92 A cross between a Donkey and a Zebra is called a Zonkey.

93 Some reindeer can journey over 3000 miles in one year.

YOU WOULD WEIGH MORE THAN TWICE AS MUCH ON JUPITER AS YOU WOULD ON EARTH BECAUSE IT HAS A POWERFUL MAGNETIC FIELD

FUN FACTS

94 A rat is able to keep swimming for three days.

95 To help them digest Eucalyptus leaves later in life, baby koalas are fed poo by their parents after birth.

96 The hippopotamus has pink milk.

97 Snakes would drown if they tried to bite underwater.

98 Goats' pupils are rectangular.

99 The Nile crocodile, while hunting for food, will hold its breath underwater for up to two hours.

100 The era from 250 million years ago to approximately 65 million years ago is called the Mesozoic Period. It is often called the Dinosaur Age since, during this period, most dinosaurs have evolved and died out.

101 Lined up end-to-end, it would take 100 earths, to go around the surface of the sun.

102 There are hot springs in some of Iceland's ice caves.

SINCE THERE IS NO WIND TO ERASE THEM, FOOTPRINTS AND TIRE MARKS LEFT BY ASTRONAUTS WILL STAY ON THE MOON FOREVER.

FUN FACTS

103 We have high and low tides due to the gravity of the Sun and Moons.

104 The Grand Canyon has rocks that are about 2 billion years old.

105 Earthquakes can be fatal, but most are so light they are not even noticed by humans.

106 The Pacific Ocean is the biggest in the world.

107 Only 1% of the world's water is usable for agriculture, residential, manufacturing, and personal needs. 97% is saline or undrinkable, and the last 2% is caught in icecaps and glaciers.

108 The weight of the Earth is 6,588,000,000,000,000 tons.

109 The only country that is also a single continent, is Australia.

110 The Earth is a little flattened at the poles, so it is not completely circular.

PEANUTS ARE LEGUMES AND NOT NUTS!

111 The 1932 winter was so cold that Niagara Falls totally froze over.

112 Plants on the Earth's surface Earth have been around for 400 million years.

113 Clouds cover about 60% of the planet at all times.

114 Some Bamboo can grow as much as a meter in just one day!

115 The Earth is between 4 and 5 billion years old, according to scientists.

116 Rainwater has vitamin B12 in it.

117 The only planet not named after a god is Earth.

118 The Dead Sea loses 8.5 million tons of water to evaporation per day.

119 In 1900, Hawaii officially joined the United States.

THE HARDEST ENGLISH TONGUE TWISTER IS BELIEVED TO BE THE "SIXTH SICK SHEIK'S SIXTH SHEEP'S SICK.

FUN FACTS

120 Earth's width is 12,756 miles (7,926 km).

121 Every second, Niagara Falls could fill 4,000 bathrooms.

122 There are more pyramids found in Peru than in Egypt.

123 In one year, the earth can have as many as 50 000 earthquakes.

124 The most sunny place on earth is Yuma, Arizona which gets more than 4000 hours of sun a year. The least sunny place is the South Pole, where the sun shines only 182 days a year.

125 The only fish that is known to blink with both eyes is the shark.

126 Sea Lions are the only known animal that can clap in rhythm.

127 Just 18 of the 250 + recognized shark species are considered to be dangerous to humans.

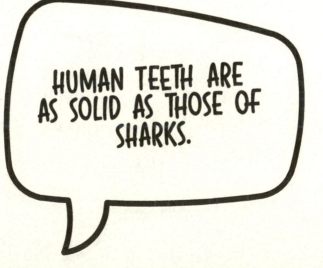

HUMAN TEETH ARE AS SOLID AS THOSE OF SHARKS.

128 Lobster blood does not have a color, but it turns blue when exposed to air.

129 For more than 400 million years, sharks have been around.

130 The giant squid has the world's biggest eyes.

131 The Giant Pacific Octopus can fit its whole body through a hole as small as its beak.

132 Dolphins can hear sounds underwater from 24 km (15 miles) away.

133 At 4 km (2.5miles) away, sharks can sense a drop of blood.

134 The dirtiest thing in a normal household, hospital, or hotel room is the TV remote.

135 Fish scales are an ingredient in certain lipsticks.

136 Household dust is composed of dead skin cells.

THE NUMBER ONE SOURCE OF ARGUMENTS BETWEEN COUPLES, IS MONEY.

137 Created around the 1940s, electronic computers were as big as a large room.

138 The first Robotics Inventions System is revealed by LEGO.

139 Central Park in New York has more than 225 000 trees.

140 The full name of Los Angeles is "The People of Our Lady of the City of the Angels of Porciuncula"."

141 The town with the most difficult name is Llanfairpwllgwyngyllgogerychwyrndrobwyll llantysiliogogogoch, and it is located in Wales.

142 The biggest wave ever surfed was as tall as a 10-story building.

143 The US United States experiences more than 1200 tornadoes a year.

144 The portrait of Mona Lisa took ten years for Leonardo Da Vinci to paint.

145 Eight percent of the population has an extra rib.

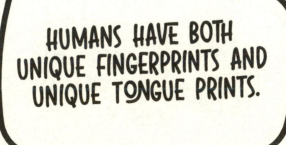

HUMANS HAVE BOTH UNIQUE FINGERPRINTS AND UNIQUE TONGUE PRINTS.

146 Fifty-nine percent of people say they look average.

147 The biggest organ of the human body is your skin.

148 Your feet create a pint of sweat each day.

149 Humans and chimpanzees share 98.8% DNA, but they still have about 35 million distinctions.

150 In a normal lifespan, the human heart beats over three billion times.

151 You can't smell anything while you're sleeping, not even extremely unpleasant or strong smells.

152 Every year the average person takes in more than one ton of food and drink.

153 There is about 78 percent water in the average human brain.

154 Your blood is six times as thick as water.

SLEEPING CAN BURN MORE CALORIES THAN WATCHING TV DOES.

FUN FACTS

155 When you're cold, your fingernails grow quicker.

156 The human tongue print is as unique as a fingerprint.

157 Your nose and ears will never stop growing as long as you live.

158 There are 67 different species of bacteria in the average person's belly button.

159 Every four weeks, you shed a full layer of skin.

160 A person will die of complete lack of sleep earlier than of hunger (death will occur around ten days without sleep while food takes a couple of weeks).

161 When talking, you use 72 distinct muscles.

162 Laughing reduces stress levels and builds up the immune system.

163 It is not possible for a human to lick their own elbow.

THE UNITED STATES DOLLAR IS THE MOST BARTERED CURRENCY IN THE WORLD.

164 Scientists say between 1 PM and 2:30 PM is the perfect time to nap, as that's when we feel tired, due to a drop in body temperature.

165 The body needs about 12 hours to fully digest a meal.

166 It takes seven minutes for most people to fall asleep.

167 An average person will sleep for 25 years.

168 53% of all women will not go out without applying makeup.

169 The human eye can perceive and distinguish more than 10 million colors.

170 Our universe has more than 125 billion galaxies. There are about 100-400 billion stars in our galaxy.

171 The moon is very hot during the day (average 224 degrees Fahrenheit) but very cold at night (-243 degrees average).

TWO OUT OF FIVE PEOPLE WILL MARRY THEIR FIRST LOVE.

FUN FACTS

172 There will be the footsteps on the moon for 100 million years.

173 Every year, more than 500 meteorites hit the Earth.

174 While asleep, you can eat at least 70 different insects and 10 spiders in your lifetime.

175 The oldest cockroach fossils are more than 280 million years old.

176 7% of the U.S. population consumes McDonalds on a daily basis.

177 Cucumbers consist of 96% water.

178 The average American diet is 55% junk food.

179 Garlic bulbs are filled with vitamin C, copper, potassium, magnesium, zinc, etc. It has 17 amino acids as well.

180 Bank of America's original name was the Bank of Italy.

MORE COCA COLA IS DRUNK IN ICELAND THAN ANY OTHER COUNTRY.